It was important to Martin, Lili's fiancé, that his cousin, Daniel, should like her. But when she met Daniel, she wasn't sure if she could ever merely *like* the sophisticated and powerful man he was. Nor was she sure that that was what he felt for her, either . . .

IMPACT

BY

MADELEINE KER

MILLS & BOON LIMITED
15–16 BROOK'S MEWS
LONDON W1A 1DR

First published in Great Britain 1986
by Mills & Boon Limited

© Madeleine Ker 1986

Australian copyright 1986
Philippine copyright 1986
This edition 1986

ISBN 0 263 75433 2

Set in Monophoto Times 10 on 10½ pt.
01-0886 – 56314

Printed and bound in Great Britain by
Collins, Glasgow

CHAPTER ONE

'TRUST Daniel,' Martin said wryly.

The helicopter blades thundered way above head-height, and yet Lili instinctively ducked as she walked beneath their whirling power, almost shocking after the peace of Antibes. She had to let go of Martin's hand and clutch at her ribboned straw hat to stop it from being buffeted off as she climbed the steel rungs into the leather-lined cockpit.

The machine was deep scarlet, with the Maison Rouge logo emblazoned in gold along the sides. It was typical of Daniel's style to have the whirlybird waiting for them at the airport, rotors already turning to whisk them off to L'Hermitage, as soon as the plane from Nice had landed.

A right royal welcome, designed to make them feel privileged? Or swift transport to a right royal beheading? By the expression on Martin's face, he didn't know, either!

The summons had been irrefutable, though. It had come in the form of a telephone call to Antibes, only six hours in the wake of Martin's cable announcing his engagement to Lili.

'We're both going to L'Hermitage,' he'd told her rather ruefully when he'd put the phone down. 'A little holiday with Daniel.'

'I thought we were going to be staying here until Le Mans?' she'd queried.

'No one refuses an invitation from Daniel,' Martin had said simply. 'Besides, we can stay at L'Hermitage right through the race. It'll save you hotel bills.' He was already heading towards his room to pack.

Lili's stomach lurched as the helicopter surged

upwards in a cacophony of sound and banked over the airport buildings towards the countryside of Normandy. Towards England, the sky was dark with clouds. Above them, so far, it was cobalt blue. Down below, less privileged Air France passengers were still filing across grey tarmac into the airport building. Lili had an odd sense of leaving the mundane behind them.

As a rising model, she'd seen something of the way rich and glamorous people lived. Martin himself led an exciting life, even since, to his disgust, Daniel had cut off his allowance. But this was something special. For the next few weeks of her summer holiday she was going to be moving in a world she'd only touched the fringes of before.

There was a style about Daniel Valais that tended to overwhelm you. It wasn't hard to see why Martin Petrov's attitude towards his older cousin was a strange mixture of hero-worship and nervousness.

'Here we go,' she said quietly. He heard her above the engine-noise.

'Not getting airsick, are you?'

'I'm just trying to adjust to the jet-set life.' She took the straw hat off, hauled one of her Louis Vuitton bags onto her knee, and fished for a hairbrush. The turbulence had whipped her long ash-blonde hair into a tangle. 'I thought riding in a taxicab was special, not so long ago. Private helicopters are not exactly what I'm used to!'

'I think Daniel wants to impress you,' he smiled.

'I'm impressed. Definitely.' The face in the mirror as she combed her hair was tanned, beautifully regular, with eyes that would be emerald but for the almost wild topaz glint in their depths. Passionate mouth, straight nose. 'Should I paint?'

'You look fantastic,' he said, blue eyes sparkling at her. 'Anyway, he likes them natural.'

'"Them",' she repeated in mock disgust. 'I'm not *them*, you male chauvinist piglet!'

'Anyway, you still look good enough to eat.'

'You're forgiven.' She snapped the bag shut sealing her own image within it, and leaned over to him. 'It must be being with you,' she smiled, touching his nose with her own. 'What's Big Brother going to do to us?'

'You mean Big Cousin. And he'll love you, I promise,' Martin said confidently.

'Will he?'

'Don't make him out to be such an ogre!'

Lili smiled. Her rugged, impulsive fiancé was always confident. Especially since Silverstone. Despite her immediate attraction to Martin when they'd first met, she'd never really taken his driving seriously. He'd seemed almost a bit of a playboy, a dilettante. Her first real boyfriend, but she'd never considered *marriage*.

Silverstone had changed all that. Suddenly, Martin's dream of a career in racing had seemed so possible. Until Silverstone she hadn't really believed in it, not deep down. When she'd seen Martin's face on television, heard the pundits describing him as a bright new talent on the endurance-racing scene—she'd started believing.

It was a replica of what had just happened in her own life. Three years of working in record shops, fashion boutiques, even a kite-factory in Tunbridge Wells, where she'd been born, and still lived—and then finding herself on the cover of *Charade*. Becoming society's darling, overnight, with people chasing you, waving contracts.

Miracles did happen. When Martin had asked her to marry him, on the beach at Antibes, she'd been dazzled. He'd seemed so much more a man, so much less just an attractive boy. When he'd proposed, she'd felt deeply honoured.

She'd said yes.

The enormity of it still hadn't sunk in. She was going to be married. Going to be the wife of a glamorous, aristocratic young racing-driver who'd swept her off her feet. Was she really ready for it all?

'Do you think Silverstone will have changed Daniel's mind about you and racing?' she asked thoughtfully.

'Once Daniel's made his mind up about something,' he replied with a grimace, 'it would take dynamite to shift it. Don't forget, he's got Magyar blood in his veins, like me.' He gave her a sly grin. 'Dynamite—or a very, *very* pretty face.'

'I've heard that tune before,' she warned. 'I'm going to be on a sticky enough wicket as it is. Don't get me involved in your family quarrels before I've even arrived!'

'Ah, but my revered cousin has a weakness for the female sex. Another Magyar trait, so I'm told! Can't resist a beautiful woman. If you were to take him aside at L'Hermitage, try and talk him round——'

'No!'

'At Antibes you said you believed in me,' he reminded her plaintively. 'If he wanted to, Daniel could make our married lives a lot more comfortable, you know.'

'That's not the point.' Her whole upringing rebelled against that attitude of Martin's towards his cousin's wealth. 'What Daniel does with his money is his affair. He doesn't owe us anything. You've got to make your own way in this life, Martin.'

'I realise that,' he said impatiently. She knew that he hated her lectures about self-sufficiency. 'But until I make a real success of racing, we won't have very much to live on——'

'Except what I could earn if I kept on modelling,' she put in, but he didn't choose to hear.

'—and if I could persuade Daniel to take me seriously, he could help out. Just a kind of loan, until I'm rich and famous.'

'He has offered you a job,' Lili pointed out. Martin's full lower lip curled in disgust.

'I'm not cut out to be an office boy in Daniel's smallest factory, Lili. You ought to know that by now.

Anyway, I've managed to find myself a job on my own account,' he reminded her proudly. 'You're so keen on self-reliance—you ought to be delighted with me!'

'I suppose I am,' she smiled. She looked out of the window and thought of the sunlit countryside of Normandy far below them.

Daniel might be a dictator, but she knew Martin's version of things wasn't quite accurate. Daniel had offered him an opening in Maison Rouge, the vast male fashion empire he'd created. Not a managership right away. He'd offered to show Martin the business from the ground-floor up. Lili, who'd had to struggle for most things in her life, knew exactly what a fantastic opportunity that would have been.

But Martin, as she also knew, was not a patient personality. His cousin's offer had seemed more like an insult than a privilege. He'd expected to slide neatly to the top.

And Daniel, in his turn, had been equally impatient with Martin's choice of motor-racing, after three years of trying various other outlets for his talents, as an alternative career.

Martin, rather naïvely, had been expecting Daniel to approve. A large proportion of the Maison Rouge advertising budget had been allocated to endurance-racing over the past five years, the red-and-gold cars becoming a familiar sight on the circuits. Daniel himself had driven the winning car at Le Mans on three separate occasions, twice in Porsches managed by Derek Brundle, and sponsored by Maison Rouge.

Not that Martin didn't have considerable talent, too. He'd been offered occasional drives in Formula 3 for Arcolex, the big construction company, at a time when he was still officially supposed to be pursuing his education.

Then, last year, he'd used the family connection to ask Derek Brundle, the Maison Rouge team-boss, for a drive. Daniel had been in Sweden at the time, on business. And Martin, having timed it just right, had impressed Derek enough to have been offered a place on the team as a novice driver—pending Daniel's decision.

Martin had been confident, despite the opposition he knew was there. 'Daniel may pay all the bills,' he'd once explained to Lili, 'but he seldom interferes with Derek's administrative decisions.'

When Martin had blithely informed Daniel of his intention of joining the Maison Rouge-sponsored team, he'd made no secret of his disapproval. But Martin had simply threatened that if Daniel vetoed him, he would go on applying to other teams until he did get a drive.

And Daniel, growling that since he was now paying Martin's salary, he was damned if he was going to keep on shelling out pocket-money to boot, had cut off the allowance he'd been giving Martin for the past four years. Considering that a novice driver's wages were fairly low, that had infuriated Martin.

Until Silverstone, Martin had only had short unimportant drives. Then one of the senior drivers had been forced to retire through sciatica, and Martin had been given his chance. And everything had changed. Or had it?

It was a complex, ambiguous situation. Daniel Valais wasn't just Martin's cousin. He'd practically raised Martin single-handed. *The nearest thing I have to an elder brother*, Martin had called him.

His parents didn't figure much in Martin's life. Lili had met his mother, Lucy, in London a few weeks ago—a brightly-painted, vacant-eyed divorcee who drank too much. His father, he'd told her, had remarried, and lived in Switzerland. He and Martin never saw each other. That was something else that had drawn them together; like herself, Martin really didn't have any parents. Except for Daniel.

She'd seen him, once, in England, just after she and Martin had started going out together. It had been a

very brief encounter; she'd gone with Martin to see him
off at Heathrow Airport, and true to form, Martin had
been late. But in those five minutes at the gate of the
crowded departure lounge, Daniel Valais had left an
indelible impression on her of power, ruthlessness, and
supreme male beauty.

Given the relationship between the two, meeting
Daniel today was going to feel unpleasantly like being
vetted, checked over for suitability to marry Martin
Petrov—and that was quite apart from any family rows
that might explode over Martin's racing. Also, Martin
was in a cocky, aggressive mood. He was ready to
throw his part in the Silverstone victory at Daniel.

'Stop worrying! Now that I'm a race-winner, he'll
have to accept that racing's the career for me.' He drew
her to him. Martin's kisses had always excited her; he
was forceful, the most glamorous person she'd ever met.
As his tongue forced her lips apart, all her doubts and
fears seemed to vanish like shadows. What did it
matter, after all . . .

Their kiss was interrupted by the helicopter banking
sharply to the right. The pilot turned to them, pointing
sideways. To the south-east of them, a town sprawled in
the sun. Almost directly below the helicopter, the
winding grey ribbon of a race-track was laid out
between towering grandstands, neat as a child's toy
some thousands of feet below.

'Le Mans!' Martin's face was alight, as though the
race-track were indeed a toy, and he a child gloating
over it on Christmas morning. 'Isn't it beautiful!'

'If you say so,' she said wryly, peering down. She
could see the distant paddock, shimmering in the heat.

'I'm going to be there soon,' he vowed. 'And I'm
going to be first across that finishing line, Lili. I'm
going to win the greatest race in the world. That'll show
Daniel what a brilliant driver I am.'

'Oh, such modesty!' The gentle teasing had become
part of the relationship, her response to his eternal

optimism. Lili watched his eager profile as the chopper flew over and past the famous race-track, thinking for the thousandth time how good-looking Martin Petrov was, as though his colourful and romantic family background shone through his face. 'Just drive carefully at Le Mans.' She touched his cheek. 'I don't want to lose you down there, darling.'

'Pessimist!' he accused.

She only smiled, looking out. 'I lost both my parents,' she'd once told him when he'd accused her of lacking self-confidence. 'And then I lost my foster-mother. Self-confidence is something I've had to teach myself, Martin. It doesn't come to me naturally.'

Checking his boisterous nature was like touching wood. Averting the evil eye. Or was that ridiculously superstitious?

She smiled down on the sunlit landscape. The rest of her own year was studded with important commissions. There was money in the bank, a new white and blue Escort Cabriolet garaged at her flat in Tunbridge Wells. She'd worked hard this year, hard enough for Mandy Collins, her agent, to give in when she'd wanted a holiday with her fiancé. The pre-honeymoon, as they'd called it, had only just begun, thrilling, dazzling. And not even the prospect of meeting Daniel could cloud her joyous mood.

'We're approaching the Hermitage estate,' the pilot called to them over his shoulder.

Lili felt her heart quicken as she stared out of the window. Down below them, in the late afternoon sun, vivid green lines of perfectly tended apple-trees stretched out in orderly rows. Along the wide avenue of pines, a chattering troupe of forty or fifty tanned young people were making their way homewards. Some waved casually, obviously quite used to being overflown by a scarlet-and-gold helicopter.

'The orchards came with the estate,' Martin explained. 'This is quite a famous cider-producing area—and Daniel doesn't like to see anything lying idle.' He smiled. 'Actually, the stuff's quite drinkable—and that's the opinion of a beer man!'

'It's vast,' she said in awe, as fields and meadows swept beneath them.

'Over this rise,' Martin said, 'and then you'll see the house.'

She knew she'd never forget her first sight of L'Hermitage.

A great château of pale golden stone, ringed by lawns of velvety turf. Lebanon cedars, dark and massive enough to have been planted when the first stone was set, towered like sentinels in the idyllic paradise of the Renaissance parkland all around. An arched stone bridge spanned the moat that ringed the château itself; beside it, a weeping willow trailed its long skirts in the still, dark water.

'Dear Heaven, it's stunning,' Lili breathed. Martin was watching her with a wry expression.

'I thought you'd be impressed.'

As the helicopter drifted over the moat, she was able to look down on to the weathered grey tiles of the complex, multi-faceted roof, down into the cobbled courtyard, into the very heart of the château. Like staring into the heart of another age, another world. A handful of white doves, disturbed by the clattering intrusion of the helicopter, exploded into the air, and dispersed towards the woods on the gently landscaped hills beyond.

Then they were sweeping low over the other side of the great building, down towards a sweeping, gravelled drive where another helicopter, also in Maison Rouge colours, was already standing. Beside it, two beautiful cars were parked, a red Ferrari and a silver Rolls-Royce.

The formal gardens beyond were ablaze with flowers, a succession of white marble fountains spraying a dozen arcs of diamonds into the evening air among the roses.

Lili stepped out of the helicopter on to the crunching pink gravel. The whirring blades above were chopping their way into silence, letting the vast peace of L'Hermitage envelop them. Wealth? This was something beyond wealth. To own an estate like this must be . . . She couldn't find words.

'Well.' Martin's expression was an odd mixture of apprehension and pleasure as he stepped out behind her. 'You've just arrived at the nearest we'll ever get to a family home.'

She closed her eyes, inhaling the heavy scent of the cedars on the warm air. The sea-salt of Antibes was still on her golden skin from this morning's swim, the last swim of their holiday . . . And now she was here, in this exquisite, fertile corner of Normandy. So much had happened to her lately that she knew she was going to have to keep a very tight rein on her emotions from now on.

'*Soyez le bienvenu, M'sieu Martin, soyez la bienvenue, Mam'selle!*' The old man who came scurrying out of the gabled doorway was beaming with delight. He kissed Lili's hand as though she were a princess, swept a bow to Martin, then trotted round the machine to help the pilot unload their suitcases.

'Whatever your family had in Eastern Europe,' she said to Martin as he took her arm, 'it couldn't have been more beautiful than this.'

'I guess not. But we had family estates in Romania that went back centuries. Daniel only bought L'Hermitage eight years ago.'

'When he was twenty-six,' she murmured incredulously. 'It's stunning.'

'You're going to get on with Daniel, my love. Anyone who likes the old place gets a gold star in his book.'

They followed the old man into the entrance-hall. Lili stopped in awe, and let her gaze travel up the curving staircase, to the gallery above, its panelled walls hung with magnificent paintings; and then up to the three

immense crystal chandeliers which hung like a frozen
waterfall from the high, cross-beamed and inlaid
ceiling.

'He'll want to show you round the château himself,'
Martin told her. 'There's plenty of time for that, later
on. He'll be in the drawing-room now.' He led her
towards one of the double-doors that led off the hall,
and pushed it open.

The reception-room was ablaze with the dying sun,
the golden light splashed on tapestries, oak panelling,
the luminous swags of exquisite brocade curtains. A
man in a charcoal grey suit had been writing at a
leather-topped Queen Anne desk as they came in, but
at the sound of their footsteps he turned and rose
capping a gold Parker.

Daniel Valais was taller than Lili had remembered,
taller even than Martin, older and tougher-looking, his
thick, dark hair streaked with silver at the temples. And
he was still the most attractive man she'd ever seen.

To her immediate relief, there was no surface tension.
He gave Martin a warm hug, then held him at arm's
length, muscular brown hands gripping Martin's
shoulders. 'The prodigal returns,' he growled in mock-
anger. 'You want the world, I think. Do you expect to
live like a playboy, win Le Mans, and become a
responsible husband, all at the same time?'

'Just watch me,' Martin chuckled. 'You look fit as
hell, Daniel.'

'I try, *mon cousin*, I try.' Lili was nervously conscious
of Daniel's formidable eyes turning to her. High
cheekbones that suggested his Slavic origins, a strong,
sensual mouth, a heart-stopping face that was ruthlessly
male enough to present a direct sexual challenge to any
woman.

'Lili.' His voice was husky, giving the French lilt to
her name. He was Swiss by birth, she knew, but he
spoke with only the faintest tang of an accent. 'Am I to
call you *cousine*, then?'

'I'd rather you called me Lili,' she said, trying to smile.

'My lovely Lili, then. Let me look at you.' Strong hands closed around her own, his palms warm against hers. Imprisoned there, she had no choice but to submit to an explicit head-to-foot inspection. His eyes were wide, slate-grey, shockingly direct. Like an insolent caress, they drifted upwards across her legs, hips, the swell of her full breasts against the cream silk. As they met her own, Lili couldn't stop her heart from contracting in the iron grip of an electric current.

'I *see.*' There was the ghost of a smile somewhere. He'd seen that moment of reaction in her own eyes, and was laughing at her! 'It is easy to understand why Martin has been keeping you hidden away all this time.'

Nervously she withdrew her fingers from his grasp, hoping he hadn't noticed that her palms were suddenly moist. Her body was tingling as though his glance had been a rough masculine caress all across her naked skin. 'Martin hasn't been hiding me at all!'

'No?' The slight smile didn't waver, nor did those extraordinary eyes. 'You are to be married to my cousin, and yet this is only the second time I have met you in three months. How does that come about?'

'We needed a little time together,' Lili began, her cheeks flushed at the implied rebuke in his remarks. 'We haven't been avoiding you, *Monsieur* Valais, I promise.'

'Don't bully her.' Martin protested, his face tightening. 'I'm the one you ought to be shouting at, Daniel.'

'I'm not shouting at anyone,' he said gently. 'Least of all Lili.'

Again that lilting accent to her name!

'In any case,' Lili said, knowing she mustn't let her spirited nature get riled by someone as sophisticated as Daniel Valais, 'you are perfectly right, *monsieur*. We should have come to you a long time ago. Martin has told me many times how much in your debt he is.'

'Indeed.' Damn him, why wouldn't he look away, let her drop her eyes! There was some primitive force in his stare that reached out to her, as irresistible as brute physical compulsion. Then he suddenly smiled, any coldness melting like ice in the sun. 'You're not what I expected, Lili Bergman. I should have paid more attention to you when we first met, it seems.' He reached for her left hand, holding it up enquiringly. 'No ring?'

'We haven't got around to that yet,' she said, knowing the elegant curves of her cheekbones were still flushed like a schoolgirl's. The truth was that Martin, as a novice driver, didn't have that much money. She'd have been content with a tiny diamond, but he'd insisted they wait until he'd earned enough to buy her something spectacular.

'I see.' Apparently amused, he turned away from her to Martin. 'You never change, *mon ami*. Always forgetting the most important details. If I were you, I'd get that ring on her finger before someone else does.'

'Maybe I will.' Martin looked sullen at the comment, but was obviously trying to put a brave face on it.

'And now I think a drink is called for.' Daniel turned to an ornate ormolu cabinet and opened the doors.

Behind his back Martin gave her a silent *phew* of relief that the first awkward moments, which she knew he'd been dreading, were over. Lili wasn't quite so relieved. Maybe there were a lot more awkward moments in reserve. Especially for her—later!

'*Alors.*' He handed them each a glittering tumbler with a golden heart of Cognac. 'We'll drink to your future happiness. *Félicitations!*'

The brandy burned like fire in Lili's throat. 'I haven't seen you since Silverstone,' Martin said casually, his eyes betraying that he was eager for his cousin's praise.

'I couldn't make it to the race,' Daniel said in a neutral voice. 'I had to convene a directors' meeting to discuss my proposal to buy out *Textiles Delaval.*'

'But you watched on TV?' Martin was almost pleading. Lili felt a pang of pity for him; he was so much the younger brother, begging for Daniel's approval. 'Your meeting couldn't have been that important?'

'I was somewhat busy trying to persuade my board that we needed to spend twenty million pounds,' he said drily. 'You sometimes forget that endurance-racing is merely a part of Maison Rouge's advertising campaign.' He tossed a copy of the *Financial Times* at Martin. 'If you read the front page, you might be interested to see that I succeeded, which means we now have our own major supplier of silks and rayons. That happens to be a rather important turning-point in the company's history.' He relented with a slight smile. 'As a matter of fact, I managed to catch some of the race, during the afternoon recess.'

'What did you think?' Martin asked eagerly.

'Not bad, *mon vieux*. At least you managed to resist the temptation to park your car in the top of a tree.'

'Very funny,' Martin grinned. Lili smiled a little tightly. She didn't care to think about Martin's bad crash at Fuji in Japan last September, when his Porsche had somersaulted over a barrier and smashed into a tree. That had been long before she'd met him, and he'd walked away from the wreck unscathed, but she'd almost been sick when she'd seen a video replay of the accident some weeks earlier.

'Derek tells me the cars are improving steadily,' Daniel said, eyes watching them both over the rim of his glass.

'That's not the only reason I won,' Martin said, a little snappishly. 'It was also good driving.'

'Good driving on the part of Christian Seberg. A little help from you.' The comment was pointed, but fair. In endurance-driving, as she'd had to learn, at least two drivers, and sometimes three, shared each car. The fact that his co-driver had been the veteran Christian

Seberg, an ex-Porsche works driver, tended to get neglected in Martin's account of the Maison Rouge victory at Silverstone. 'It was Christian who won, Martin. You were lucky to have been allowed to help out.'

'I'd say I did more than that.' Martin was hurt. 'Derek was delighted with me. At least I'm getting somewhere in racing, huh?'

'As I said, you were lucky. It's an exciting—if dangerous—hobby. It brings occasional great rewards. Like Silverstone. But as an occupation, it's reserved for a very select few.'

'And you don't think I'm one of them. Or is it that you can't face up to the possibility that I might turn out a better driver than you?' The defiant expression on Martin's face made Lili's heart sink. He wasn't going to start a row with Daniel, not on her first formal meeting with the man, surely?

'No, it isn't that,' Daniel said quietly, though his brows were ominously lowered now. 'But racing is a dangerous mistress, Martin. Like the sea. You are only flirting with her. And she does not forgive those who flirt. Sometimes she even kills her favourites. Those whose hearts are not in the sport——' He shook his head. 'They stand no chance.'

'How do you *know* my heart isn't in it?' Martin demanded passionately. '*You're* the one who flirts! You only race when you feel like it. I'm the one who wants to be a professional driver!'

'It's a game to you,' Daniel said with infuriating calmness. 'The way the Sorbonne was a game to you. The way many things have been a game to you, Martin.'

'You can't believe I'm serious about *anything*,' Martin retorted. He turned to her, pale now. 'Lili, I'm sorry I brought you here. You shouldn't have to go through all this!'

'You're right,' the older man said, a smile easing the

grimness out of his mouth. 'We aren't being exactly hospitable to your beautiful fiancée. I haven't even kissed her, the way a cousin should.'

She'd opened her unsuspecting mouth to say something as he slid an arm round her slender waist and kissed her parted lips. His kiss was hard, warm, bone-meltingly intimate. It paralysed her, her eyes widening into dazed pools as she felt his tongue touch hers with wicked assurance, a caress that would have been erotic between lovers, was shocking between strangers!

Her heart was pounding as he released her, and she knew her colour would be high, as though she'd been excited by his challenge, rather than otherwise.

'Steady on,' Martin said, smiling reluctantly despite himself. 'Every girl I've ever brought here has fallen in love with you, Daniel. But I'm not giving up this one!'

'Then you'd better look after her,' he said in that growling, husky voice. His eyes were searching hers again, as though for that intimate reaction.

'I intend to!'

'Good.' His eyes flicked to Martin's now. 'I'm sure Lili understands why I'm against your racing,' he said. 'You're practically my only living blood relative, Martin. And I happen to love you like a brother. I don't want you to end up raw hamburger.'

Again, Lili had to wince. He had a terrifying way about him sometimes. You couldn't be indifferent to that prowling, panther-like quality in Daniel Valais. You had to respect the raw power being fed into the big, lean frame.

'I don't intend to end up raw hamburger,' Martin said, his dark mood lifting now. 'You've forgotten what it's like to be twenty-two, Daniel.'

'It hasn't been *that* long,' Daniel replied, one dark brow arching.

'Yeah, but what you also forget is that you've got nothing to prove. I *have*!'

'Well, whatever you want to prove, the race-track isn't the place to do it. Come on, we've had this argument before.'

'We have,' Martin said ruefully, 'and you never change.'

Lili let out a silent pent-up breath of relief that the quarrel was rumbling into the distance now. She could still feel that kiss on her lips, haunting and sensual. The clothes he wore had the elegant simplicity that comes very expensive; the anthracite-dark suit was magnificently cut, the pearl-grey shirt obviously hand-made out of Shantung silk. He'd have been a supreme male animal in any clothes. In this setting, he was stunning.

She glanced at Martin, noting his complex expression. The sparrowhawk and the king eagle, she thought wryly. Would Martin ever soar to the heights Daniel had reached so easily?

'If you don't like motor-racing, *chérie*, you're going to be very bored over the next twenty years.' With a jolt, Lili realised that Daniel had turned back to her, and her voice was a little breathless as she answered.

'I'm not exactly sure what to expect,' she admitted, glancing at Martin's smiling face. Was he going to let Daniel call her *chérie*? 'I watched the Silverstone 1000 on TV in Paris, but that's about my total experience. I wouldn't even know how to get the bonnet open on my own Ford.'

'It's in Daniel's blood,' Martin put in. 'You wouldn't think it to hear him lecture *me*, but they say he's one of the best and bravest amateurs on the circuit!'

'It amuses me,' Daniel said with a shrug. 'But I am not so foolish as to regard it as a career.' He turned to Lili, grey eyes lit by the sunset. 'I learned to drive in my mother's Bugatti, in the Alps, when I was five years old.'

'That sounds very romantic,' she smiled at him.

'Daniel's mother and my father escaped from behind the Iron Curtain in that car,' Martin said, his expression misty. 'I wish we still had that Bugatti, Daniel.'

'It was destroyed in the accident,' he replied quietly. A silence fell for a moment. That hadn't been a very tactful remark on Martin's part—she knew that Daniel's mother had died in that motoring accident. She looked down, remembering her own life. Then Daniel laughed gently. 'I'm keeping you both from showers you must be dying for. And the kitchen is in a furore, preparing a grand dinner in your honour. Come along, *mes enfants*, and I'll show you to your rooms.'

Where his hand touched her arm it seemed to leave five spots of fire. Lili walked with Daniel, her legs feeling oddly shaky.

She'd sometimes wondered whether Martin's picture of his cousin as an overbearing dictator who liked to dominate people was quite fair. It had only taken an hour in his company to tell her that Martin had—if anything—understated things!

Not that she was intimidated. This was going to be no Norman conquest for Daniel Valais, not if she had her way! And the holiday she'd been so looking forward to might not be as relaxing as she'd hoped, after all . . .

CHAPTER TWO

THE storm must have broken around one a.m. Through her dreams she'd been aware of the thunder and the beating of the rain for half an hour, getting steadily worse. It was the crash of her casement window bursting open that woke her with a start.

The curtains were already soaked, and flapping heavily in the gale. Lili switched on her bedside lamp, and clambered out of bed, shivering in her thin nightie. She'd been dreaming she was on a ship at sea, a tossing ship whose gold-braided captain had watched her with Daniel's dark eyes. She was still smiling sleepily at the fancy as she tried to unhook the wet curtain from the corner of the casement.

The world outside suddenly erupted in blinding white light, and the simultaneous crash of thunder was so loud she felt it vibrate to her very fingertips. At the same moment, her bedside light flickered out.

Blackness. Her heart beating against her ribs, Lili blundered in the pitch darkness for the main light switch. She found it, but it, too, was dead. The lightning must have struck a power line nearby. And the rain was still streaming in at her flapping window, the curtain hopelessly entangled.

'Damn,' she whispered, trying to fight down her irrational panic. There was no torch in her bedside cabinet.

She'd thought it amusingly old-fashioned when Daniel had put her and Martin in bedrooms so far apart that she doubted she'd ever be able to find her way to his, but right now it wasn't so funny.

Another elemental flash of lightning was followed by a huge crash of thunder, right overhead. The storm-centre was passing directly over L'Hermitage. Pulling her dressing-gown around her shoulders, she fumbled for the door-handle, and padded out into the corridor on bare feet. It was completely black outside.

'Hullo?' Her nervous voice sounded almost child-like. 'Is anybody there?'

'Lili? Are you all right?' To her intense relief she recognised the low call as Martin's.

'The wind's blown my window open.' She shivered unhappily in the cool air. 'And the power's off.'

'Sssh. You'll wake the whole house. Power failures sometimes happen here.' His hands were strong and warm as they found her.

'I couldn't find a torch.' She guided him into her room, and sat on the end of the bed as he untangled the curtain and latched the window securely against the beating rain.

'There.'

'Thank God you came,' she said with a sigh. She got up, arms reaching out for him in the dark. 'Your dictatorial cousin seems to want to keep us as far apart as possible for some reason.' She snuggled up against his reassuring bulk for comfort. 'Do you think he imagines we're a pair of passionate lovers?'

'I'm sure he does.' His breath was warm against her neck, his arms sliding around her. 'You smell wonderful.'

'And I thought you didn't appreciate women's perfumes,' she teased. Her fear was ebbing away rapidly. Maybe it was the storm that continued to rage outside, but there was something strangely exciting about this secret, dark embrace. They really knew so little about one another, had never been as intimate as this. 'Do you realise we've never shared a bedroom before?' she asked. 'I'm beginning to think I might rather like it!' She lifted her lips to his, seeking a kiss.

'What about my dictatorial cousin?' he said softly.

'Daniel's probably fast asleep, dreaming of his millions,' she smiled. 'Anyway, it's none of his business.' She was the one who'd always resisted Martin's pushing before, yet there was something about the night that was making her mischievous. She ran her hands appreciatively across the iron-hard muscles of his arms and shoulders. 'As a matter of fact, I was dreaming of him when I woke.'

'Indeed.' The way he said it made her giggle. 'What kind of dream?'

'A nice one. Are you going to tuck me up?' she invited. 'It would be the gentlemanly thing to do.'

It was sheer wickedness that made her press up against him, the soft swell of her breasts brushing provocatively against the hard power of his chest.

His reaction was instantaneous, utterly male. She'd never known such strength in his arms before, nor such passionate authority in his kiss. She felt her knees go weak as his hands roamed through her hair, caressing the surrendering arc of her throat, pressing her body against him. His tongue invaded her mouth, a kiss of such autocratic expertise that she felt with sudden certainty that she wasn't in Martin's arms, *couldn't* be. She'd been too caught up in her predicament until now to notice how tall he was, how much stronger than Martin—and that husky voice could sound very like Martin's, especially when it was pitched softly——

'Daniel!' She struggled free of him, the blood still surging through her veins like molten gold. 'It is you, isn't it!'

The soft laugh mocked her from the darkness. *'Oui, je regrette beaucoup, chérie. C'est moi.'*

'How *could* you!' Thank heavens for the darkness which cloaked her scarlet cheeks, and hid those compelling grey eyes from her. 'You deliberately took advantage of me!'

'I plead guilty.' He seemed to be able to see in the dark, like a leopard, for his touch on her cheek was wickedly sure. 'But you were a maiden in distress, not so? I could hardly refuse to assist. It would have been ungallant.'

'*Ungallant!*' Her heart was thudding, every nerve in her body tingling with anger at the way she'd been fooled. 'Just how far would you have gone?'

'As far as any gentleman would go.' He was kissing her again, but she could feel the smile on his warm mouth. 'There, *ma petite*, don't take it so seriously. When I realised you thought I was my cousin, my only intention was to tuck you up, as you so sweetly requested——' She ground her teeth in embarrassment. '—and leave you to fall asleep in ignorant bliss. Or should that be blissful ignorance? My English isn't always as good as it should be.'

'Your English is perfect,' she snapped, feeling too upset to spar with him in the dark. 'I don't intend arguing with a man I can't even see, Daniel. Thank you for shutting my window. And now, if you'll excuse me, I'm getting into bed.'

She clambered between the cold sheets, pulling them up to her chin. How humiliating, how infuriating to discover she'd been passionately kissing the wrong man in her bedroom.

'*Violà.*' As if to bring her blood to the boiling-point, he was tucking her in, sure hands smoothing the tumbled hair away from her face. She could hear the richly amused laughter in his deep, husky voice—how could she *ever* have mistaken him for Martin? 'I'm sure you'll have another nice dream tonight. *Bonne nuit*, Lili.' His kiss was soft as a feather on her brow. She clenched the sheets in her hands as fiercely as though she were pulling that thick, crisp hair. At the door, he paused. 'My cousin is a very lucky man,' he said softly. 'I envy him.'

Then the door closed quietly. Outside, the rain was still beating at the window. The whole painful episode could almost have been another weird dream but for the bruised feeling on her lips, and the fact that she knew the curtains were still soaked.

What a thing to happen on her first night at

L'Hermitage. Could anything more embarrassing have been dreamed up by the imp who superintended Murphy's Law? No doubt Daniel now imagined her relationship with Martin was far more sensual than it actually was.

She sat up in bed with a sudden thought. 'You have really gone?' she said into the dark. 'Haven't you? Daniel?'

The pattering rain mocked her anxiety. Still taut with resentment, she pounded the pillow into shape, and rolled on to her side. She was remembering the candle-lit dinner he'd given them only hours ago.

It had been dazzlingly romantic. Daniel had brought all his potent charm to bear on the evening. His talk had fascinated her, had them both laughing helplessly at times, even though she still hadn't learned to look into those deep grey eyes without feeling the gooseflesh creep across her skin.

Had he sensed her instinctive response to him? She had the uneasy impression that he'd seen some chink in her armour. That kiss might have been his way of testing that chink. If she hadn't recognised him just now, what *would* have happened?

It didn't bear thinking about! Deliberately, she steered her mind to a neutral setting. A studio somewhere in London. Matt black back-cloth, a set of soft side-lights. The atmosphere relaxed, smooth. Everything working well, the film unrolling steadily in the automatic Hasselblad.

Another peal of thunder had her peaceful studio blown to shreds. She rolled on to her other side, as hot now as she'd been cold a minute ago. Sleep, she knew, was going to be a long, long time in coming.

The next day was stormy, too. The bad weather—which, as Martin acidly commented, had come down from Britain—seemed to have settled in over L'Hermitage. It helped to cement Lili's mood of electric resentment towards Daniel. How was she ever going to meet his eyes again without squirming like a schoolgirl? God, it made her hot with humiliation to think of the way she'd snuggled blissfully up to him, teasing him into the flaring passion of that kiss.

She'd slept late, and was relieved to find that Daniel had already left for Paris by the time she got to the breakfast table. Should she tell Martin about that midnight visitation? No, denial came instantly. Martin might not understand the ease with which she'd been deceived. In any case, it would only provoke more tension between all three of them. Unless Daniel told him about it, she'd keep the incident a private memory!

'I'll show you round the old place,' Martin invited, and there seemed little other choice, given the weather. Martin wasn't a very knowledgeable guide—he obviously didn't share his cousin's expertise with art and antiques—but Lili was content simply to wander round in awe.

L'Hermitage was a fantastic house. 'House' seemed an inadequate word—yet 'castle' or *château* didn't capture the very real sense in which L'Hermitage was a home. Beautiful and grand, but also comforting, intimate, a place to raise a family in.

Yet Daniel lived here alone. Or maybe not so alone? Martin took her to the vast ballroom, and spoke of the place being filled with important and distinguished guests at week-ends, of the women who flocked round Daniel like moths round a candle.

She pulled a wry face. It was very easy to see why. There were a lot of women who would find his particular brand of arrogant domination fatally attractive.

It was simply unfortunate that she wasn't one of them.

Or maybe it wasn't so unfortunate, after all. If she'd been in any way susceptible to Daniel's charm, staying here might have put rather a strain on her relationship with Martin!

Daniel was back from Paris by early afternoon. She heard the helicopter arrive, but decided to stay in the seclusion of the library where she'd been leafing through the collection of seventeenth-century texts that Daniel had built up. She wasn't exactly eager to meet him again, not so soon after last night, anyway, so she stayed curled up on the red-leather settee in the soft glow of the reading-light.

Her desire for privacy was not to be respected, however. Martin must have told Daniel where she was, and he came to find her.

'I hadn't quite seen you as a bookworm,' he said softly, walking over to where she sat.

'I can read without moving my lips,' she couldn't help retorting, hastily snatching off her glasses. His normally imperious mouth was curving into a slow smile as he sat down beside her, superbly elegant in a dark suit and grey tie.

His proximity seemed to affect the pulses at her throat and temples, the blood racing faster through her veins. He had something, a power, a magnetism, call it what you will, that was almost frightening.

'You sound annoyed with me,' he murmured, the slight lift at the end of the sentence making it a mocking question.

'Not at all,' she said in a carefully controlled voice, and pretended to be fascinated in the book she was reading. He reached out to take it from her and study the title-page

'*Anatomy of Melancholy?*' he enquired gently, one eyebrow lifting. 'Hardly appropriate reading for a beautiful young woman.'

'It interested me.' The flush she'd been dreading was spreading across her skin. Against her will, her eyes had strayed to study the masculine, sensual mouth that had kissed hers so expertly in the darkness. 'I like old books.'

'So do I.' He laid the book firmly out of reach. 'I

trust you didn't have any more trouble with your window last night?'

She cursed herself for reacting to his wickedly amused glance. 'None at all, thanks,' she gritted out, trying to sound casual. 'I suppose I should thank you for—er—coming to my rescue.'

'It was a pleasure.' His voice was husky with suppressed laughter. 'All of it. I trust you've forgiven me?'

'I'm trying,' she said, glad of her thick lashes as they covered her eyes.

'*Bon.* I did have a reason for interrupting your reading, *chérie*. I want your professional opinion on something.'

'What?' she asked suspiciously.

'This.' He was holding a slim corked test-tube with a typed label. 'It's an aftershave which was developed by a Swiss perfumery. My research department want Maison Rouge to market it. I'd like to know what you think of it.'

'What difference would my opinion make?' she retorted, taking the glass tube reluctantly.

'You never know,' he smiled.

'*Men* wear aftershave,' she reminded him. Her opinion could mean nothing to him, and she had the distinct feeling he was patronising her!

'For the benefit of women. And you belong to the generation that will buy the product, after all.'

She shot him a dry look. The age-gap between them was definitely there, piquant and intriguing. It probably explained some of the tension she felt towards him. 'I'm sure you've had this stuff market-tested by experts,' she shrugged, 'but here goes.'

She uncorked the tube. The aftershave was very strong, musky and unusual.

'You have to let the alcohol evaporate,' he commanded. He tipped a drop on to her wrist before she could protest, and rubbed the spot dry with warm fingers. The unexpectedly personal contact made her jump, gooseflesh prickling the fine hairs of her forearms.

Slate-grey eyes studied her. 'You're very nervous, *chérie*.'

'Not at all,' she snapped, wishing he wouldn't touch her like that—it was probably bad for her heart! She lifted her wrist and sniffed cautiously. The fragrance was distinctive, an unashamedly erotic smell that was somehow very modern.

'You like it?' he challenged.

'It isn't very subtle.' She sniffed again, recognising that the aftershave would certainly make most women's hearts beat a little faster. 'But it's effective,' she admitted grudgingly.

'That's what I thought.' He smiled into her eyes. 'I'm going to give it the go-ahead.'

'What are you going to call it?' she asked as he took the test-tube back.

'Probably something feline,' he speculated. 'The advertising people like the name *Panther*.'

'That's not very subtle, either,' she said pointedly.

'It's not a subtle market.'

'I notice you haven't put any on,' she pointed out.

'If I did, Martin might develop the unworthy suspicion that you and I had been kissing and cuddling in here.' The glint in his eyes mocked her expression of shock. 'Besides, I have my aftershave especially blended by Saint Germain in Geneva.'

'I see,' she replied, refusing to be put down by such potent one upmanship, 'so this stuff is strictly for the peasants?'

'It's for young men who want a distinctive aftershave, but who can't afford Saint Germain,' he said gently. He took her hand, and raised it to his lips. Fascinated despite herself, she watched his long, dark lashes close as he inhaled the fragrance at her wrist. 'No,' he said softly. 'It doesn't suit you. Your skin has a natural perfume all its own, Lili. I noticed it the first day you came here—as soon as I kissed you.' His lips brushed her beating pulse as gently as a butterfly's wings. 'You always smell beautiful.'

'You're—teasing me,' she said unsteadily, trying to tell herself that he didn't affect her when he talked like this, touched her like this.

'I assure you I am not.' His eyes met hers. 'But your heart is beating very fast, little one. Has something disturbed you?'

'No!' Suddenly feeling that she was going to faint and fall helplessly into his arms, Lili pulled her hand away and stood up, her mind reeling. 'The aftershave is very nice. Where's Martin? I want to talk to him about something.'

He watched her for a long second, those deep eyes seeming to know every emotion that quivered beneath her skin. Then he smiled, and rose.

'He's in the drawing-room. We'll go and meet him shall we? It's just about time for afternoon tea.'

The canopy above her was white lawn, embroidered with foxgloves and wild flowers, beautiful and feminine.

Lili drifted into wakefulness in the huge four-poster bed, and stretched luxuriously, her slender body refreshed after a deep sleep.

She padded to the window on bare feet and threw the wide casement open, and leaned out joyously. Surely it was one of the most marvellous views in the world. The storm had receded at last, and the formal gardens were brilliant in early-morning sunlight. Beyond, the gently rolling hills of Normandy were etched against a vivid blue sky. On such a day as this, she could even forgive Daniel!

A tiny maid poked her head round the door to announce that *le petit déjeuner* was being served downstairs in ten minutes, and did *mam'selle* have any laundry or ironing to give her?

The sunny breakfast-room was empty when Lili got downstairs, feeling light and summery in a Helga Moritz cotton dress that was a cornflower blue to match the sky. She helped herself to cornflakes and cream, giving the eggs, mushrooms and bacon on the silver chafing-dishes a miss.

'All by yourself?'

There was no mistaking the dark, husky voice. She felt her heart miss a beat as she turned to look up at Daniel.

'Yes,' she nodded. 'Martin's still—er—resting.'

'He hasn't done very much to tire him out,' Daniel observed drily. He looked stunning; tailored charcoal slacks fitted perfectly over his slim hips and long, muscular legs, and the cream shirt was made from the kind of ultra-lightweight silk that crushes to a mere handful. It emphasised the breath and power of his shoulders, the hard lines of his narrow waist. 'Sleep well?'

'Perfectly,' she said in a carefully controlled voice. 'Can I pour you some coffee?'

'Please. Oh, and by the way—this was in the morning's post.' He laid a French edition of *Cosmopolitan* next to her plate. 'Have you seen it?'

'The swimsuit pictures!' she guessed, and he nodded. 'I've only seen the rushes,' she admitted. Daniel helped himself to a croissant, and sat opposite her, his back to the window. He had obviously come straight from the shower, his dark hair slicked backwards, emphasising the height of his bronzed cheekbones and the disconcertingly level stare of those grey eyes.

She hated her glasses, but they were more or less essential for reading. She slipped them out of her pocket, put them on, and flipped excitedly through the glossy magazine to the fashion section.

The shots had been taken in a London studio at the end of April, while Martin had been preparing for Silverstone. It had been snowing lightly outside as she'd posed on fake beach-sand under searing spotlights. The collection of minuscule metallic swimsuits was exquisite, and decidedly erotic.

Jerry Momsworth had taken the pictures, and they were well up to his usual brilliant standard. They were revealing enough, however, for her to wish Daniel hadn't seen them. That thought almost took the edge off her pleasure.

'Do you like the shots?' Daniel enquired calmly, watching her face over a bone-china coffee cup. 'The quality is excellent.'

'Yes,' Lili nodded, slightly embarrassed at the thought that she might appear narcissistic. Unlike some other models she knew, she had no such self-love. Anyway, as emperor of Maison Rouge, he'd know that the woman in the photographs, long-legged, taut-breasted, a cliché of tanned skin and superb, sexy figure, wasn't *her*. It was an illusion, an invention of the camera and the fashion world. 'They're good. But Jerry's the one who really deserves the credit, not me. Jerry Momsworth,' she explained, 'the man who took these pictures. He's a gifted photographer.'

'He is indeed. I'll mention his name to my publicity department.' It was a throw-away line, dropped casually. Yet she knew instictively that Daniel would do exactly what he said. Among all the complex information turning around in that powerful brain, the name of Jerry Momsworth had been noted and carefully filed. 'It's not every day I have a *Cosmopolitan* model at my breakfast table.'

'It's not every day I model for *Cosmopolitan*,' she laughed breathlessly. Seeing herself in the really big magazines always gave her a special kick, and by the look in his eyes, Daniel understood that.

'Before I forget.' He dropped something on her side-plate. 'You said you wanted to explore the district today. You'll need transport.' The heavy key-ring was in the shape of a rampant stallion in solid gold. 'The keys to the Ferrari,' he explained laconically. 'I think it's more your style than the Rolls. Drive it anywhere you like. Just don't let Martin get behind the wheel.'

She closed slender fingers round the smooth golden thing. 'You'd let me drive your Ferrari,' she said incredulously, 'but not Martin?'

'I won't even let Martin drive my tractors,' he observed coolly. 'The last time I did, it cost me four thousand francs to have the barn repaired.'

She had to giggle. 'He likes to be creative.'

'He likes to be destructive sometimes, too. Can I ask you a favour?'

'Of course,' she invited.

'Take off those glasses.'

'Oh! They aren't very flattering, are they?' For some reason last night came into her mind again. She slipped them off, laying them on the table, and then looked directly at him with just a hint of defiance about the poise of her head.

'Thank you,' he said softly, eyes travelling in unselfconscious appraisal across her face. 'I like to see you eyes, Lili. They're very beautiful.'

'That's hardly an original line!' The impudent remark was out of character, but Daniel knocked her off-balance so easily that she felt she needed some kind of defence.

'Perhaps not,' he agreed, looking as though he were amused by her spirit. He turned to his croissant. 'I sometimes find Martin difficult to understand,' he remarked. 'What makes a red-blooded young man laze in his bed when there's a highly desirable woman obediently waiting for him?'

'I'm not exactly "obediently waiting" for Martin,' she retorted, stung by the tone in his deep voice.

'Oh?' He eyed her with wickedly laughing eyes. 'You're not the type to love, honour and obey?'

'The ceremony has been amended to "love and to *cherish*",' she said pointedly.

'And that's the way you feel about Martin?'

'Of course I do!' He had a disconcerting way of slipping those flat questions into the conversation. At least there had so far been no mention of Martin's driving career.

Flustered, she reached up to adjust the ponytail at the back of her head. She was unaware that the action had pulled her thin cotton dress taut over the uptilted tips of her breasts, until Daniel's hooded eyes told her so.

Everything she did seemed to emphasise the unspoken tension between them! Flushing, she dropped her arms hastily enough to make him smile. There was a disturbing arrogance in the way he didn't bother to disguise his interest in her as a woman. She had no control over his desire, but at least he could obey the rules. She was his cousin's fiancée, after all, not simply another pretty face at the breakfast table.

She'd been afraid of his anger before they'd come to L'Hermitage. If she feared him now, it was for another reason altogether.

'It pains me greatly, but I have to dash.' He gulped a last mouthful of strong coffee, and rose, fluid as a leopard. 'I'm due in Paris at nine thirty——' he glanced at his gold Rolex '—which means I'll have to take the helicopter instead of the Rolls. I'll try and be home early, though.'

She nodded, suddenly aware that his departure would be like the sunlight going out of the day.

'I'm organising a little party for you and Martin, by the way. I want you to meet some of my friends.'

'That's very kind.' She watched the sinuous lines of his body as he shrugged on an impeccable doeskin jacket. Maybe when you were the head of a giant company, you could afford to arrive at work in slacks and a leather jacket. Especially if you'd arrived in one of your own private helicopters.

'Thursday night. Just a few friends. Harold Lazenby will be here.'

'Oh?' She pricked her ears up at the name of probably the most influential female-fashion designer in the business.

'No doubt you'll have plenty to discuss.' With deceptive swiftness he was towering over her, one brown hand on the table, the other gripping the back of her chair. She stared up, heart thudding, into that magnificently male face. 'You won't be bored all day?' he growled softly.

'Not with Martin here,' she said, prompted by some inner mischief.

'In which case I shall leave you to him—the undeserving young pup. I presume we're kissing-cousins by now?'

His mouth closed on hers, warm, demanding, moulding against her yielding lips. If she'd been connected to a polygraph, she thought wildly, every bodily function would have peaked like Everest. Why did his kiss have to be so potently sexual!

That familiar bruised feeling was on her lips as she watched him stride out of the room, her pulses ebbing slowly down to normal. If she'd had any idea that Daniel was going to affect her like this, she'd have stayed as far away from L'Hermitage as humanly possible.

True to her expectations, the distant sound of the chopper firing up was like the sun going behind a cloud. He was the sort of man who left a vacuum behind him. A man of such potent energy, such vividness . . .

Like a child, she puddled her cornflakes absently with the silver spoon. He could make you feel pain or joy, just with a few words. Easy to imagine how he'd made himself a millionaire long before thirty. Easy to understand how powerfully he affected Martin.

As if on cue, Martin bounced into the room in a Duran Duran T-shirt and faded jeans. He hadn't shaved, and his bristles scrubbed her painfully as he gave her a boisterous kiss.

'Hiya, babe!'

'What a contrast!' she had to laugh as he loaded his plate with bacon and eggs.

'Between who?'

'Between you and your sophisticated cousin, you unshaven thing,' she told him, watching him gulp his breakfast down. He had the appetite of a growing bear-cub.

'And which do you prefer?'

'You—when you don't have egg all over your chin.' She smiled as he wiped himself clean.

'So,' Martin wanted to know, nodding thanks as she filled his coffee-cup, 'what do you think of our Daniel?'

'Would you be terribly upset,' Lili sighed, 'if I said he rather terrifies me?'

'You mean you don't like him?' Martin asked, glancing up from his plate.

'I don't think we're destined to become soul-mates,' she smiled at him.

'Good. That suits me just fine. What have you and Daniel been talking about?' he wanted to know.

'Just breakfast-time things. He's organising a party for us.'

'Did he say anything about me?'

'Not much,' she had to admit, thinking guiltily of that expert kiss.

'Anyway,' Martin decided, 'he seems to be in a lot better mood than I anticipated. Which also suits me just fine. I'm going to ask him to give me my allowance back,' he explained, looking at her with appealing blue eyes. 'I could really use it. Why not bring it up next time you see him?'

'Don't be silly,' she said, halfway cross, halfway amused. 'I can't ask your cousin for money on your behalf, Martin!'

'You'd have more chance than I would.'

She changed the uncomfortable topic. 'Did you dream of me, handsome?'

'Nope.' A whole rasher of bacon went down. 'Dreamed of winning Le Mans.'

'How romantic,' she sighed. 'I'm beginning to see how I fell for your suave charms in Florence.' She pushed the copy of *Cosmopolitan across* to him. 'Have a look.'

He held the page down with the back of his fork, eyes widening. Wow! Is that *you*!'

'You ought to know by now,' she said wryly.

'I haven't seen that much of you in real life,' he gaped, looking from the glamorous images to her. 'Wow-wee! Do women actually wear these things?'

'I'm not sure,' she confessed. 'You'd have to have the right sort of setting.'

'And the right sort of figure,' he breathed in awe. He turned to the end of the brief feature, eyes wide. 'Which you've *got*. Am I really going to marry all this?'

'All what?' she smiled.

'All these curves and sexy bits. What is this rag?'

'It's not a rag,' she rebuked him incredulously, 'it's *Cosmopolitan*.'

'Ah. The big time, eh?'

'You could say that,' she said, not sure whether to be amused or irritated by his gaucheness. 'The big time for *me*, at any rate.'

'Then we ought to celebrate,' he said decisively, pouring himself tea. 'Ever seen Mont St Michel?'

'You mean it?' she said, eyes widening in delight.

'If we set off early enough. It's about an hour's drive from here.'

'Oh, Martin!' She'd never seen the fabulous citadel that became an island at each high tide, but she'd always wanted to. 'Daniel's given me these.' She showed him the golden key-ring.

'Ah,' he grinned. 'In which case, it's only half an hour's drive from here.'

'Not with me at the flight-deck.' She stuck out a pink tongue at him. 'I'm not to let you near the wheel. Big

Brother's orders.' She jumped up, happy and eager.
'Can we swim?'

'If it's warm enough. But not if you're going to be
wearing one of these golden G-string things!'

'I've got a very demure one-piece upstairs,' she
promised. She blew him a kiss, and ran to get it, leaving
him poring wistfully over the photographs.

They arrived back from a blissful day to find Daniel
just climbing into a Range Rover on the gravelled
drive. He paused to lean on the door, grey eyes warm
on Lili as she got out of the Ferrari.

'Had a nice day?'

'Wonderful,' she sighed happily. 'Martin took me to
Mont St Michel.'

'And she drove all the way,' Martin added ruefully,
coming round to join her. He leaned forward, brushing
sand out of his unruly hair. 'Wouldn't let me near the
wheel. She takes you seriously, Daniel!'

'I'm glad one of you does.' Daniel smiled. His eyes
took in Lili's slim figure. 'I'm going down to the
orchards. Are you two too tired to come?'

'I've seen your mouldy old orchards a dozen times.'
Martin demurred. 'Take Lili, I'm going for a shower.'

'It seems you've been handed to me,' Daniel said with
a faint smile. 'Would you like to see the trees?'

She hesitated, then something made her nod. 'Yes,
I'd love to.'

'*Bien.*' He swung the door open for her. 'Hop in.'

'Don't bore her to death.' Martin stuck his head
through the window to kiss Lili on the cheek. 'And
don't give her too much Normandy cider to drink. I'll
see you when you get back.'

'That boy has no appreciation of the finer things of
life.' Daniel smiled as they drove through the gates
towards the green sea of apple-trees. 'After all I've tried
to teach him, too.'

'You live in one of the most beautiful places in

France,' she sighed, looking out of the window. 'In the world.'

'You must have Norman blood,' he commented. 'Do you like L' Hermitage?'

'It's the most beautiful place I've ever seen. I don't know what more I can say.'

'I don't think there is anything more to say,' he said gently. He reached for her hand, raised it, and touched it to his lips. *Merci*, Lili. I'm glad you like it. I want you to think of it as your home.'

The unexpected gesture had melted her, filled her with a warmth that stopped any more words from rising to her throat for a moment. It was a magnificent evening. The sun was low over the distant hills, and the light had a clarity she'd seldom seen in England.

She'd been meaning to say something to him for the past couple of days. Now seemed the right moment.

'I hope you aren't still angry with Martin about— having not having brought me to see you earlier,' she said hesitantly, 'It's not that he doesn't care what you think. He's very much aware of how kind you've been to him.'

'I never was angry,' he replied easily. 'I was just a little concerned that Martin might have picked a wife I could never get along with.'

'And now that you've seen me?' she couldn't help asking shyly. 'Do you think you'll get along with me?'

He glanced at her, a slow smile curving along the finely chiselled lips. 'You tell me,' he invited. 'Do we get along?'

'Very well,' she nodded. The dying sun cast golden lights into her green eyes. 'At least, I think we do. I hope we do.'

He stopped the Range Rover at the edge of the orchard. 'What if we get on too well?' he asked, reaching into the glove-compartment for a wooden-handled clasp-knife.

'I don't think that's possible,' she smiled.

An ironic eyebrow tilted. 'And I don't think you can be so naïve.' He tapped her nose gently, then climbed out of the Range Rover.

Feeling like a child, Lili followed him. Everything he said had a more sophisticated meaning than she was used to. Of course she wasn't that naïve. She simply didn't want to accept that more sophisticated, more disturbing, implication.

He wasn't like the people she was used to, bright, shallow people whose words usually meant little. He was different, different even from Martin Petrov. Adult. Powerful. A man who meant what he said, who could do what he threatened . . .

'The trees were in a bad way when I bought L' Hermitage,' he said, parting the delicate leaves to study the ripening apples. 'I had to do some fairly drastic pruning, and I was afraid that some of them would die. It seems I did the right thing, though.'

'Martin said you hated to see anything lying idle,' she said, watching him thoughtfully. He moved so purposefully, yet with such grace, he'd make any other man look clumsy. 'Is it really a profitable business?'

'Oh yes,' he said, passing her a glowing apple with a smile. 'The cider is good. I have to make it pay, or else it would just be a rich man's hobby.'

The apple wasn't sweet yet, and he grinned at her expression. 'Go on, spit it out. Don't be such a lady.'

'I've never thought of myself as a lady.' She spat the sour fruit ruefully out. 'It looked so delicious.'

'They will be in a few months. And you're a lady, *chérie*. Every inch.'

He took her arm to walk down the rows of trees, the apples glinting like uncut jewels among the leaves. The evening stillness was broken only by the cawing of a flight of homeward-bound rooks in the fleckless sky. She was all too aware of his hard body next to hers, the velvety touch of his fingers against her skin.

A friend of hers had once modelled pearls with a

purring, full-grown black panther as a bed-mate. She'd called the feeling indescribable, but Lili thought she might have an inkling right now.

'When exactly are you and Martin planning to marry?'

'We haven't decided.' Lili looked down at her own ringless hand on his arm, wishing they'd set a definite date. Daniel wasn't the sort of man who'd admire vagueness.

'Soon?'

'Yes, soon. I think.' Typical of Martin, once he had her agreement to marry him, not to be precise about when. 'We're not in any special hurry.'

'You mean *Martin's* not in any special hurry.' He paused to weigh a cluster of apples in one long-fingered hand, then turned to study her with cool grey eyes. 'Is that right?'

It was, but she covered with a white lie. 'To tell the truth, we reached the decision such a short time ago that we haven't really discussed it.' She smiled tentatively. 'We must seem ridiculous to you.'

He shook his dark head. 'Just young—and rather deliciously disorganised. Who looked after you when your parents died, Lili?'

'Until I was nineteen I lived with my mother's sister.' Auntie Joan had been a spinster, yet Lili knew no one could have been a kinder or more loving mother to her.

'Has she met Martin?'

'I thought you knew,' she said carefully. 'Joan died three years ago.'

Daniel's eyes stayed on hers. 'An orphan twice over, then.' He said it gently, almost sadly. There was a brooding, ironic slant to this man's soul, Lili realised suddenly. Something profound and profoundly experienced.

She thrust away the sadness. This wasn't the time for it. 'Yes, an orphan twice over,' she said briskly, not wanting his pity.

'Martin didn't tell me. I'm sorry.'

'There's nothing to be sorry about.' She shrugged. Why hadn't Martin told Daniel anything about her? Sometimes he was so casual! His indifference to things like that would make Daniel think her just another of Martin's easy girlfriends. 'Your parents are dead, too, aren't they? It happens.'

'I'm surprised you can be so cool about it,' he observed, eyes narrowed.

Cool was the very last thing she was. She deliberately avoided discussing Joan's death with other people for the simple fact that it usually ended up with her in tears. And she didn't want Daniel Valais to see her crying right now.

'Life can be cruel to people who are too vulnerable,' she replied obliquely.

'And that's the lesson you've learned?' It was almost a statement rather than a question, said in the same husky voice.

'I know what I want,' she gave him by way of an answer.

'And you want Martin.'

She turned to face him. 'That makes me sound very calculating,' she said, trying not to be hurt by his tone. 'It isn't like that at all.'

'Then how is it, exactly?'

'How long is a piece of string?' she challenged. 'You can't quantify something like love.'

'What I want to know,' he said silkily, 'is whether the two of you have anything more than sex to draw you together.'

'How dare you——'

He held up a hand to silence her angry retort before it came. '*D'accord*, I'm sorry, I shouldn't have asked that.'

'You had no right to,' she said tightly, feeling cruelly insulted. If Daniel thought she was some kind of vampire who'd hooked Martin with sex, he couldn't be more wrong. They hadn't even made love yet, though that hadn't been for want of Martin trying. She'd nearly succumbed, especially in those first exciting weeks. But as things stood, their relationship was as chaste as something out of a Victorian novella.

She'd never even said *I love you* to another man. Despite all the men who'd taken her out, desired her, she was still a virgin.

Still a virgin. And possibly still very naïve about the world.

'I've said I'm sorry, Lili.' His strong hands reached for her shoulders, turning her to face him. 'I mean it.'

'Look,' she said quietly, looking at him with eyes like sunlit topazes, 'I'm beginning to get the feeling that now that you've had a chance to weigh me up, you find you don't trust me or approve of me. Is it because I'm a model? Or because you think I'm not aristocratic enough to join your family?'

'I happen to think that Martin's been a lot luckier than he deserves,' he said bluntly, and for some reason her heart contracted again at the way he looked at her. 'And you would grace the highest family in the land, *chérie*.'

'But you still don't approve,' she challenged, determined to have it out with him, here and now.

'I'm concerned,' he said carefully.

'Concerned that I'll distract Martin from the career you want him to follow?'

'In part,' he acknowledged, bowing his dark head. His black hair was thick, almost over-long. It emphasised his mâle, animal magnetism. 'You give Martin a certain—what shall I call it? A certain solidarity. Two against one, to put it more plainly.'

'From what I've seen,' she told him drily, 'Martin needs all the help he can get. You don't fight fair, Daniel!'

'No,' he agreed with a hint of a smile. 'I believe the end justifies the means. Come, I'll take you to see the cider-presses.'

CHAPTER THREE

LILI was silent in the Range Rover as they drove into the golden glory of the sunset. She was still shaky after that little interrogation, but at least she'd given as good as she'd got!

The vista was magnificent. The orchards of L' Hermitage stretched out into a rolling landscape of blue hills, etched here and there with the dark spears of pine-tree and cypresses, or the tangled wild olive. She could smell the ripening apples on the air, a smell heady as first desire, and underneath that the sweetness of musk-roses from the distant gardens of the château.

The storage-buildings had new orange-tiled roofs, and their walls had been freshly rendered and whitewashed. By the arched entrance, a drinking-fountain played merrily. Here, too, she guessed, Daniel had been active.

In the long, cool chambers, the cider was stored in casks by the hundred, bottles by the thousand. It was an impressive sight, and Lili walked down the steps in awe. 'How much cider is stored here?'

'I've no idea.' He was enjoying her surprise. 'A few hundred thousand litres, I imagine.'

'I thought it was more or less a side-line for you,' she said, turning to look up at him.

'It was—at first,' he confessed. 'Now it gives me more and more pleasure. One day, Lili, I might sell Maison Rouge and retire here to L' Hermitage, and become a gentleman farmer. It's a very civilised life.'

'Somehow I can't imagine you retired,' she told him.

'I hope that's a compliment?'

'I suppose it is. Wouldn't you miss the cut and thrust of big business?'

It took him two seconds to weigh up his reply. 'No,' he said simply.

They walked down the echoing galleries, Lili studying the names and dates stamped on each cask, the great archaic stone cider-presses that had now been superseded by electronic machinery.

'How did you first meet Martin?' he asked casually.

'It was in Florence. In April.' She almost sighed as she remembered the clear spring sunlight washing like silver over the city, the first kiss they'd shared by the banks of the Arno. Had Daniel ever fallen in love? A hundred times! 'That was just after the race at Monza.' He watched her slim fingers as she ticked off the days. 'April the twelfth, to be exact. I'd just finished an assignment for Palombino Fashions, and he was celebrating after Monza. I think the team had done quite well.'

'They took fifth place,' Daniel supplied.

'Yes, that was it. Well, some friends took me to a smart disco, a sort of nightclub. Martin was there with some of the other drivers.'

'Love at first sight?'

'No——' She hesitated. 'Not exactly. Love came later. But we were attracted at first sight.'

'Attracted.' He seemed to be weighing the word for all its meanings. 'How deeply attracted?'

'Well,' she smiled, 'I've agreed to marry him.'

His eyes narrowed. 'And you're sure you've made the right decision?' Without waiting for her to answer, he pushed open an oak door leading to a room like an old-fashioned laboratory. 'Half the secret of making cider lies in the blending,' he told her, giving her a fluted glass from the rack. 'I'm lucky to have an expert called André Lamont working for me.' She watched as he filled the glass with golden cider. 'Try that,' he invited.

What had he meant by that last question? She sipped cautiously, trying to look as though she had an inkling as to what she was supposed to be looking for. The cider was heady, intoxicatingly delicious.

'I'm no authority,' she smiled, 'but that's wonderful!'

'It's going on sale this month. This one's a little drier.
See what you think.'

'Mmm.' It was fine on her palate, the dryness
underlaid with a summery fragrance of apples. 'That's
very subtle.' She looked across the scored oak table into
his deep grey eyes, and smiled. 'Like its maker. Why all
the carefully spaced questions?'

He stared for a moment, then threw his head back and
laughed softly, appreciatively. 'Am I so transparent?'

'No.' She finished the cider. 'But I get these intuitions
about you. You're worried about Martin, aren't you?'

'In part, yes.' He poured them both more cider, then
clinked his glass against hers. 'He's taken a wrong
turning, and I want to get him back on to the right
track.'

'Your track,' she reminded him. 'Driving may not be
what I would have chosen for him—and I know it's not
what you would have chosen for him. But the choice is
his, not ours.'

He stretched, the silk pulling taut over hard muscles.
'Martin is very young. The same age as you—but far
younger emotionally. These are very important years
for him, Lili. It's vital that he finds something he can
put his heart and soul into.'

'You don't seem to understand,' she said seriously,
'that his heart and soul are in motor-racing.'

'Forgive me for contradicting you.' He reached out to
touch her salt-tangled hair. 'Racing is merely his latest
infatuation. He's good at it, yes, good enough for
Derek to have given him a job as a novice driver. But
he lacks the dedication. He's just one of a thousand
equally talented young *pilotes* chasing half a dozen good
cars. Sooner or later, he'll get bored, Lili. And if he gets
bored on the Mulsanne, at two hundred and thirty
miles an hour, you won't have a fiancé any more.'

'He's got enough sense to know his own mind,' she
argued, though the image he'd just sowed in her mind

was a horrific one.

He shook his head, smoky eyes dangerous. 'He dropped out of university. He tried to write a great novel, but abandoned that after three months. He showed promise as a sailor, but as soon as he had to study for his navigation and radio qualifications, he abandoned *that*.' Daniel studied her unhappy face. 'I could go on, but it wouldn't be fair. It's not just that I'm afraid for his life on the race-track, Lili. He doesn't have any qualifications. No vocation. He's a jack of a lot of trades, a master of none. The world has been kind to him so far, but it won't be be kind to him for ever. If I could persuade him to join Maison Rouge, I know I could make him stick to it——' He broke off at her head-shake. 'You think I'm interfering in Martin's life, don't you?'

'I think you have his best interests at heart,' she replied. 'But you can't guide every step of his way, as though he were a—a clockwork toy on rails! What if he really *does* have the application?' she challenged. 'I know he's been irresponsible in the past, Daniel, but I really believe he's changed. I really do! What if he really *does* turn out to be a brilliant driver?'

'That is a very remote possibility,' he said, folding his arms.

'But a possibility, nonetheless? You see,' she pressed, before he could speak, 'Martin once told me that you could have been a great racing-driver yourself. He said you had the talent. But you chose business instead. Well, that was your decision. You can't force that same decision on your cousin! He had to lead his own life, find his own way!'

'Having to find your own way in life is a penance, *chérie*, not a luxury.' There was a hint of impatience in the grey eyes, the passionate mouth. 'You must know that. I want him to achieve his potential. What worries me is that if he doesn't join me, Martin will turn out a waster for the rest of his life.'

'I'm glad to see you've got such confidence in him,' she said ironically. Did Martin have any idea of his idol's opinion of him? Yet there was a thin thread of truth in what Daniel was saying, and it hurt.

'There is a family precedent,' he said, then smiled unexpectedly. 'Normally I love arguing, Lili, but with you I just can't do it. I take it, then, that you won't help me by trying to persuade him against racing?'

So that was the point of this little expedition! 'I would never try and persuade him to do anything he didn't want to do,' she said coldly. She'd rather he'd asked her to help him directly, instead of arousing her confused emotions in this way.

He drained his own glass, tanned throat rippling, and then studied her with a very male, assessing gaze. 'You have spirit. That intrigues me.'

'Right now,' she hinted rudely, 'I'd like a shower.'

His smile was annoyingly sexy. 'Then let's get back to the château.'

She preceded him stiffly, some of his words echoing angrily in her mind. A waster. A man with no convictions. It simply wasn't true!

'Lili!' his arm slid possessively round her taut waist, slowing her down. 'Don't be such a little empress. Try and see it the way I do, little one. No hard feelings?'

The evening was exquisite with nightingales. The sweet-scented Normandy dusk had deepened, and the birds' liquid song mixed perfectly with the small joyful water-sounds of the fountain. The landscape of L'Hermitage was melting into a violet haze before her eyes, and Lili felt her anger disappear with the beauty of it all.

He stopped her by a row of cypresses that had begun to sigh in the evening breeze. 'No hard feelings?' he repeated gently.

'You didn't have to treat me so—so tenderly,' she accused sadly. 'Now that I know what you wanted all along, I feel a bit of a fool.'

'Lili . . .' He pulled her to him, the broad strength of
his chest warm against her own skin, and tilted up her
chin. Lili had no time to close her lips, and the kiss was
heart-stoppingly intimate, the kiss of a man who'd
desired and made love to many women. 'If I treat you
tenderly,' he said, his voice rough and smoky, 'it's not
for any ulterior motive.' He kissed her again, as though
not trusting himself to speak any further.

For a swimming eternity she was lost in the smell of
his hair, the touch of his tongue against her own, the
almost frightening domination of his embrace. After
the emotional bruising he'd just subjected her to, his
maleness was heart's-ease balm. It was wrong, crazy
to let him kiss her like this, yet there was a driving
urge in her to go forward, not back, an impulse of
desire that was primeval, beyond any words or
reason.

He looked down at her without releasing her, dark
eyes narrowed.

'You taste of the sea,' he said, the words velvety,
husky.

'I had a swim this morning.' Her voice was little more
than a whisper. Surely he could hear her heart
pounding in his arms? All the powerful length of his
body was pressed to hers, touching her everywhere. 'At
Mont St Michel.'

'Ah.' Ironic amusement glinted beneath his thick
lashes. 'Mont St Michel. Was it beautiful?'

She nodded dumbly, white-gold hair falling like a veil
down one side of her face. He had her in a spell, a kind
of trance that she didn't want to break.

'You make me jealous.' It was the whispered growl of
a panther's mating. 'You make me ache, *ma petite
cousine.*' He kissed her again, harshly this time, so that
she moaned against his lips, her soul yearning to his
like a flower to the sun.

'Daniel, I don't think . . .'

'We've been talking about Martin all evening,' he

said, his lips close against hers. 'Maybe we should have been talking about ourselves, hmmm?'

Deliberately, he released her, his own ragged breathing telling her how much he'd been disturbed by those pagan moments. 'We'd better go, my wonderful mermaid, before we both do something foolish.'

She nodded and walked with him to the Range Rover, her legs weak and shaky, unable to look him in the face. What on earth was growing between them? If he had any idea how he had shaken her by that kiss, that touch——

Of course he knew. Just as she knew that he was sharing this swelling passion. She had only known him a few days. What was yet to come? By the pounding in her veins, it had to stop right here and now, or it was going to land her in a most terrible mess.

She sat back in the seat, knowing she had to say something now, tell him never to touch her like that again.

His hand covered her eyes, sealing them shut, and his voice was warm against her cheek. 'Not through glass,' he said, and she could hear the smile in his voice. She heard the electric window hum down, and then his hand was gone. The new moon was a thin, silver sickle in the violet sky. 'Never look at the new moon through glass,' he said.

The engine purred into life, and the headlights dazzled against the whitewashed wall.

'Or aren't you superstitious?'

The unspoken tensions between them all had been more or less submerged so far, but from that evening onwards, Lili felt them start to rise to the surface. Oddly enough, her own confusion and unease made her snappish towards Martin, rather than towards Daniel. She caught herself being sharp, unreasonably irritable with Martin more than once, and it was scarcely surprising that he responded in the same vein.

At the week-end, the atmosphere was distinctly stormy. Being away from her work was beginning to tell on Lili; she'd needed the break, but doing nothing just wasn't in her nature. There wasn't much, however, that she could do about it except tell herself to try and relax.

Daniel drove them to *Au Caneton* on Saturday night, a local restaurant which had earned itself a glittering reputation for country cooking. Lili hadn't really wanted to go, but it would have been rude to refuse. As it turned out, her premonition was disastrously correct.

The food was as excellent as Daniel had promised, and the setting was enchanting; but Martin was in an aggressive, prickly mood, and the amount of wine he was drinking obviously wasn't improving his mood. Lili herself seemed unable to shake off her own tension either.

It was a casual remark from Lili that ignited the spark. She'd noticed how easily Daniel seemed to use his left hand, and he'd informed her he was ambidextrous. When she'd asked Martin innocently whether he shared the accomplishment, his face had darkened.

'No,' he said shortly. 'I'm just a normal, left-handed human being.'

Daniel had found two pens in his jacket pocket, and he pulled the menu towards him, and with a pen in each hand, began to write.

Fascinated, Lili watched the two pens move across the paper, each scribing a different sentence. When Daniel gave her the menu, she saw that his left hand had written *Shall I compare thee to a summer's day?*, while his right hand had written. *Thou art more lovely and more temperate*.

'That's fantastic,' she gasped. 'How did you learn to do that?'

'I inherited the trait from my mother,' Daniel said with a slight smile. 'Martin is left-handed, like his father.'

Martin suddenly slammed his fork down with unexpected violence. 'Is that another jibe at my father?' he demanded furiously. Lili's mouth opened in shock at his tone, but Daniel merely shook his head.

'No, that isn't a jibe at anyone,' he said quietly.

'You never give up, do you?' Martin demanded, bitterly enough to make people at nearby tables glance their way curiously. 'You never miss an opportunity to tell everyone how superior your mother was to my father!'

'Lower your voice,' Daniel said coolly. 'You're being hysterical, Martin. I intended no slight to your father.'

'Oh no,' Martin sneered, 'not you!'

'Martin,' Lili said in a quiet voice, laying her hand on his, 'I don't think Daniel meant anything.'

'You don't know him like I do,' Martin retorted. 'He's always despised my father. Know why? Because my father happens to be alive, and his mother is dead. He blames my father for surviving!'

'I've told you to lower your voice,' Daniel repeated grimly. 'If you want to shout at me, wait until we get back to L'Hermitage.'

'Can you deny that you despise my father?' Martin shot back. His fingers were gripping Lili's tightly now, his face passionate and intent. 'Can you?'

'I don't despise Ivan.' It was said flatly, but Martin wasn't satisfied.

'Then tell me you respect him!'

Lili waited tensely in the silence that followed. Daniel's dark eyes drifted from Martin's to hers, then he shrugged slightly. 'No. I do not respect him.'

Lili almost gasped at the cold deliberation of the statement. Martin's cheeks flooded with colour.

'The truth at last,' he said thickly. He turned to Lili with a humourless smile, his eyes somehow blind-looking. 'I told you that you don't know him, Lili. Maybe now you understand what I've had to deal with all my life?' He rose, throwing his napkin down. 'I have to go to the bathroom. Excuse me, won't you?'

Lili shot Daniel a furious glance as Martin stalked across the crowded restaurant. 'Did you have to be so cruel?' she asked in an icy voice.

'No,' Daniel said calmly. 'I could have lied. But he would simply have pressed until he got the truth.'

'You're very cold-blooded, aren't you?' she accused, desperately sorry for Martin. 'Don't you think it might be better to put your damned pride second for once, and not hurt him?'

'He hurts himself,' Daniel replied, grey eyes holding hers. 'I simply happen to be the nearest stone wall available for him to bang his head against.'

'That's exactly what you are,' she snapped, 'a stone wall! You don't care how much Martin suffers, how much you break down his self-respect!'

'Now you're being hysterical,' he said, his tone far sharper than it had been towards Martin. 'I've looked after Martin all his life—I care about the boy.'

'He's *not* a boy,' she threw at him, the words tumbling out of her frustration and unhappiness. 'He's a man—though maybe you prefer not to notice that! And maybe you have looked after him all his life. But now that he's an adult, don't you think it's time you stopped trying to control his destiny? Can't you just accept that he doesn't want to join Maison Rouge, and let him run his own life?'

'When I see him behave the way he's behaving tonight,' Daniel said shortly, 'the last place I want him is in my company.' He took a deep breath, as though coiling his temper down like a steel spring. 'You're very ill-advised to support him when he throws these tantrums, Lili. He needs to grow up.'

'Ill-advised?' she repeated in a voice that shook with anger. 'Martin is my fiancé, Daniel. I intend to support him in *everything* he does! And when I see him being systematically humiliated——'

'*J'en ai assez,*' he said sharply, reaching for her shoulder. Fingers like steel rods bit into her flesh, giving her one sharp shake that rattled her teeth. 'That will do, Lili. I realise that you're tense and confused, but enough is enough.'

Her anger was gone as though he'd pulled the plug. She sat in sullen silence, staring at her plate, aware of the inquisitive stares of other diners.

'Be sensible,' he said softly, touching her cheek with his knuckles. 'And try and understand yourself.'

'What do you mean?' she asked in a low voice.

'You know exactly what I mean. There's a reason for your feeling unhappy, but it's not because I'm cruel to Martin.'

She looked up to meet an expression in the deep eyes that turned her heart over inside her. Before she could say anything in answer, Martin had rejoined them. His expression was slightly easier now, as though his outburst had somehow reduced the pressure in some mental abscess.

'Sorry I flew off the handle,' he said sulkily, sitting down. 'Too much wine, I guess.'

'*De rien, mon vieux,*' Daniel smiled, offering Martin his hand. 'I hope your appetite isn't spoiled for dessert?'

'No.' A reluctant smile crossed Martin's face. 'You must try the local pastries,' he told Lili, 'they're delicious.'

'I will,' she nodded. Martin's good humour was clearly flooding back, and he launched into reminiscences about the last time he and his cousin had eaten here.

The party was on an even keel again. But that last sentence of Daniel's kept haunting Lili right through the meal, and well beyond it into the night.

Monday was brilliantly sunny, and the staff had laid a cold salad lunch out on the lawned terrace, a perfect spot sheltered from the light breeze by severely geometrical topiary hedges. Daniel had brought two guests to L'Hermitage, an English couple, Sir Edward Lawrence and his wife.

Lili had been rather awe-struck to find that Sir Edward was the head of one of the biggest and most prestigious British chain-store groups. He and Daniel had obviously just reached an agreement to launch a range of Maison Rouge clothing on the British market over the next eighteen months, and though she didn't know the details, it was clearly a significant deal.

'I saw your pictures in *Cosmopolitan* yesterday,' Lady Lawrence said, leaning across to Lili while the men were laughing at some joke. 'They're quite lovely.'

'Thank you.' Those wretched photographs again! Why couldn't they have been the elegantly flowing evening-dresses she'd modelled last month! 'I generally wear rather more than that,' she smiled.

'Oh, you have a beautiful figure,' the older woman told her, 'there's absolutely nothing to be shy about. Besides,' she added with a twinkle, 'those bathing-costumes are a lot more interesting than the prudish things we wore when I was your age.'

'I thought they were great,' Martin put in, catching the drift of the conversation. Since the row at *Au Caneton*, she'd been getting along with him much better, almost as though the argument had purged the air between them. 'I think I'm going to buy Lili one.'

'You'd never let me wear it,' Lili scoffed, 'even if I wanted to. You'd run a mile!'

'Would I?' He waved at a solitary bee that had wandered their way from the rose-beds. 'We'll see.'

'It's so perfect here,' Lady Lawrence sighed, refusing the waiter who was offering more lobster mayonnaise. 'This must be one of the loveliest spots on earth. I think your cousin has the most exquisite taste.'

'Daniel doesn't do too badly for himself,' Martin conceded. Daniel turned to them with a smile.

'What's that about Daniel?'

'Martin thinks you don't do too badly,' Lady Lawrence said solemnly.

'I'm very gratified to hear it,' Daniel said, equally

grave. His grey eyes found Lili's, his pupils dark and appreciative, making her pulses jump, as always. 'I don't think Martin's done too badly for himself either.'

'Hear, hear.' Sir Edward raised his glass in Lili's direction.

'Take a swap?' Martin grinned. 'Lili for L' Hermitage?'

'I might take you up on that,' Daniel murmured in his deep voice. His eyes had dropped to study her full mouth, as though re-living that intoxicating kiss in the twilight a few days ago. 'I just might.'

'Look,' Sir Edward chuckled, 'you've got poor Lili blushing like a girl.'

'You monster,' Lili accused Martin, her cheeks indeed hot, 'you wouldn't swap me for an old château, would you?'

'It's very tempting,' Martin teased. 'Especially since I'm on such short rations these days.' He turned to Daniel pleadingly. 'When are you going to restore my allowance, Daniel? I'm a man with responsibilities these days.'

Lili winced at the bad timing of the remark, but Daniel leaned back, considering his cousin over his wine-glass.

'Very well,' he said gently. 'I'll offer you another exchange. Your allowance back—in full—if you'll set a date for the wedding.'

In the silence, a blackbird started to sing from a nearby hedge.

'The wedding?' Martin looked uncertain.

'Exactly.' Daniel nodded for the butler to refill their glasses. 'You can't offer to marry Lili, and not set a definite date.'

'Quite so.' Sir Edward studied his glass of wine against the sunlight. 'This Chablis of yours is excellent, Daniel.'

'Well?' Daniel said silkily, still watching Martin's unsmiling face. 'When's it to be, *mon vieux*?'

Lili was painfully embarrassed now. What wicked impulse was making Daniel put Martin on the spot like this? If he was doing it out of a sense of duty towards her, he was placing her in a distinctly uncomfortable position.

What was even more humiliating was Martin's miserable expression. You'd think he was being asked to set a date for his own execution!

'Well——' He scratched his head. 'Maybe sometime at the end of the season. When I'm established as a driver.'

'The last race is at 'Kyalami, December the first.' Daniel's accuracy was ruthless. 'What about December the eighth? You can marry in the cathedral, and we'll hold the reception here at L' Hermitage.'

'No fear—I can just imagine all my scrounging friends descending on L' Hermitage like locusts. I was thinking of holding the reception on board Concorde.' But Martin's face was hunted, despite the lightness of his words. 'December? That's only six months away!'

'If *I* were going to marry Lili,' Sir Edward smiled, 'I'd be a bit keener than *that*, my boy.'

'Yeah.' Martin's blue eyes met Lili's guiltily, then looked away with a touch of embarrassement. His sour expression lightened with a conscious effort. He swallowed. 'Right. December the eighth, then.' He gulped his wine down, and looked back at Lili. This time his eyes were clear, determined. 'That suit you?'

'It suits me fine,' she said in a quiet voice. The little exchange had been weirdly uncomfortable. She'd wanted to jump up and shout that it was her life they were discussing so casually. Yet it was what she wanted, wasn't it?

'Great!' He leaned across the damask tablecloth to kiss her resoundingly. 'I'll try and give you a victory at Kyalami for your wedding-present. Now,' he turned on Daniel, 'your side of the bargain. I take it my allowance is going to be back-dated to when you cut it off?'

The Lawrences burst into laughter, but Lili wasn't even slightly amused. In fact, there were tears pricking just under her lids. Why had that hurt so much? Because it had been so lightly, so jokingly handled? Or because she'd had some stupid, unformed notion that Daniel hadn't wanted her to marry Martin?

Of course there could never be anything between her and Daniel; even if she wasn't engaged to Martin, he was far too powerful and attractive a man to bother with her.

But maybe there was some impulse in every woman that made her glad to feel desired. Even by a man other than the one she was going to marry, and even if it was a purely physical desire, just a flirtation. Selfish, and vain, yes, but she was a woman like any other.

She felt his eyes on her, but didn't look up. The hurt inside was because he'd just pricked her vanity. She'd had a crazy fantasy that he wanted her. By consigning her so casually to Martin, he'd shown that fantasy up for what it was—a presumptuous affectation.

Lili had never felt lonelier or more vulnerable than at this moment.

'Congratulations.' She felt his warm fingers cover her hand for a moment. 'The next thing is Lili's ring.'

'Come on,' Martin protested, 'I've just wangled my allowance back. I'd be back to square one if I had to buy her a ring.'

'Get it on tick,' Lady Lawrence advised, amused by the tone in his voice.

'No chance,' Martin groaned. 'My revered cousin happens to be my guarantor, and he's refused to let me get into any debt.'

'Any *more* debt,' Daniel emphasised. 'I haven't forgotten that business with the yacht you fell in and out of love with. She's still sitting at a marina not far from here, with a "For Sale" sign tacked to the mast.'

'Don't tell Lili all my sins,' Martin pleaded. 'If you're so keen on the idea of Lili having a diamond, why don't you give me the money for one?'

Lili glanced up to meet Daniel's eyes. They were narrowed, smoky. Inconsequentially, she remembered that first night at L' Hermitage, when they'd kissed in the dark. Just how accidental *had* that been? 'If I buy Lili the diamond,' he said gently, 'I'll also marry her.'

'In which case Martin gets L'Hermitage,' Lady Lawrence reminded them.

'I believe he *would* think it a fair swap,' Sir Edward said, stroking his white beard with a smile in his eyes. 'I've always said Daniel was only waiting for the right girl to come along, haven't I, Daphne?'

'Yes, but Lili isn't the right girl,' his wife pointed out. 'She's going to marry Martin.'

Lili smiled absently, letting the conversation wash over her. She was thinking about that pitch-black, stormy night in her bedroom. Had she really mistaken Daniel's voice for Martin's? There was a resemblance, yet Daniel's deep voice had a husky, distinctive note that was unmistakable.

And when he'd taken her in his arms, had she really confused Daniel's iron-hard strength and height with Martin?

Maybe she'd been fooling herself for a long, long time. She'd felt an attraction towards Daniel, right from the first brief encounter at Heathrow. Since coming to this golden château, she'd let that attraction develop unchecked. What had she been thinking of? She'd been unbelievably naïve. It was time she started realising that she could be caught in a situation of considerable ambiguity.

She looked across at Daniel, bone-meltingly handsome, tanned, potent.

'She's an excellent negotiator,' he was saying of a business acquaintance. 'She has these baby-blue eyes and little-girl-lost expression, but she can wheel and deal with the best of them.'

Wheeling and dealing. It was Daniel's stock-in-trade. It would be fatal to let herself get caught up in more webs and traps of fantasy!

It had been an almost bewilderingly event-filled year for her. In January she'd jumped straight into the deep end. Resigned from the boutique and signed on with one of the best modelling agencies in London.

The next three months had been the busiest period in all her four working years. Suddenly she was a model, no longer an anonymous shop-girl dancing patient attendance while richer women bought themselves unsuitable clothes. She'd been busy with a commission of one sort or another for three months solid.

At the beginning of April there had been the *Charade* cover, and all the ballyhoo that had accompanied it. It had been so exciting! The feeling of having arrived was like wine, it rushed to your head. You thought you'd never grow tired of seeing your own face on every news-stand. Mandy Collins, the agency boss, had been flooded with requests for Lili Bergman. If only Joan had been alive to share that moment of triumph.

That first weekend in April, she'd flown to Florence to work for Luigi Palombino, the best and brightest of the offers that had come in as a result of the *Charade* cover. She'd met Martin a week later, had stood up when he asked her to dance, had laughed at the coincidence of their both being English.

She glanced across the table at him. Well, after five years at a Lincolnshire public school, Martin Petrov was practically English, a lot more English than French or Swiss or Romanian!

He was laughing at something Daniel had said, his face merry and bright now. Martin had been the climax of a long upwards spiral of excitement. The ultimate glamorous male—international, aristocratic, a handsome young racing-driver with laughing eyes and broad shoulders.

It would have been odd, she'd once reflected wrily, if she *hadn't* fallen for him!

They'd been attracted to each other immediately,

and had seen a lot of each other over the next two weeks in Italy.

They'd come back to England on the same flight at the end of April. She'd stopped in London to model swimsuits. Martin had gone on to Silverstone to rehearse for the Silverstone One Thousand.

They'd seen each other as often as they could until the race, finding excitement in each other's company.

Then the Maison Rouge team had taken first place at Silverstone.

She'd had to watch the race on TV in France, where she'd been working under contract, and had sat with thumping heart as the commentators had enthused over Martin's driving, had predicted a bright future for him.

Two days after the race, Martin had flown out to join her in Paris. One of Martin's Swiss cousins had a villa at Cap d'Antibes, and it was there, still dripping after a swim, that he'd looked up at her and said, 'Will you marry me?' Maybe it had been the euphoria of his recent co-victory, maybe it had been the relaxed setting, but they'd both burst into laughter a second later . . .

'You're not allowed to be so quiet,' Sir Edward commanded, breaking into her reverie. 'Beautiful creatures have responsibilities, you know.' He put her glass firmly into her hand 'Drink up. You're put on earth to brighten life up for the rest of us drab things.'

'Exactly,' Lady Lawrence agreed. 'I've been dying to meet Lili Bergman, and all I've heard so far has been boring men's talk of contracts and cartels. Tell me what it's like to be a fashion model.'

Lili smiled, and joined the conversation.

The Lawrences left for Charles de Gaulle airport in the afternoon.

Lili had watched the helicopter rise slowly off the drive, high into the cloudless sky, its red and gold body tilting like a bright drangonfly as it banked over the château and picked up air speed towards the east.

Excusing herself from Martin and Daniel, she went to
her bedroom, changed into a black leotard, and headed
for the fully-equipped gymnasium and sauna in the east
wing. It seemed a good opportunity to get rid of some
excess tension and keep herself in shape at the same
time. Since leaving London, she hadn't been counting
calories as strictly as she ought to have done, and if she
wasn't careful, it was going to show in Barbados.

She was scheduled to be back at work by the
Thursday after the 24-hour race at Le Mans. It was an
important commission, one that Mandy Collins had
worked hard to get her—a glamorous television
advertisement, part of which would be filmed in
Barbados. If the client liked it, the advertising agency
had promised at least three more follow-up ads for Lili,
and the pay was going to be excellent.

She'd met the executive producer, Nick Makropoulos,
in London; and though he'd assured her that the
directors would guide her through, she was nervous
about her first real experience of television work.

Hauling on the rowing-machine feeling her muscles
stretch and pull, she let her mind drift back over the
events of the afternoon. There was still an uncomfortable feeling inside her about the way Daniel had
bulldozed Martin into deciding on their wedding-date.

So she was going to be Mrs Petrov on December the
eighth. Why was she still so depressed about it? After all,
the decision to marry had been taken a long time ago,
on the beach at Antibes. Even earlier, perhaps, during
the weeks of their courtship.

Yet many things had been wrong with this afternoon,
and one of them had been the look in Martin's eyes.

There was a footfall behind her.

'I take it you're satisfied now?'

She leaned on the handles of the machine, panting,
and looked up at Martin. 'I didn't hear you come in.
What do you mean, "satisfied now"?'

'You've got what you wanted.' His expression wasn't

pleasant, his mouth bitter. He hitched himself on to the pommel-horse, thrusting his hands into the pockets of his jeans. 'I wondered what you and Daniel had been talking about the other night in the orchard,' he said, making it a sneer. 'I might have guessed. You came back looking very flushed and starry-eyed. Now I know why.'

'What are you getting at?' she demanded, not wanting to believe what she was hearing.

'I'm getting at December the eighth,' he retorted. 'Our wedding day.'

She brushed the golden hair away from her damp temples, feeling a chill replace the warmth in her veins. 'You think I asked Daniel to put pressure on you?' she asked incredulously.

'Well?' He drummed on the leather with his heels. 'Didn't you?'

'I don't think you know me very well,' she said in a quiet voice.

'I don't think I do,' he agreed with another humourless smile. 'Though I can't say I blame you. It was as good a way as any of getting that ring on your finger.'

'*Martin.*' She swung herself off the rowing-machine, the handles closing with an angry pneumatic hiss. 'You're teasing me, aren't you?'

He looked taken aback as she faced him, a taut figure in black, her beautiful face tense with shock. 'Didn't you ask Daniel to put the strong-arm on me?' he asked with lingering defiance.

'I don't even feel like dignifying that question with an answer,' she said furiously. 'But since you've asked it— no, I did *not* ask Daniel to twist your arm.' She'd been annoyed with Martin before, but never as angry as this. 'You thought—you actually *imagined*—that I'd been complaining to your cousin about the fact that we hadn't set a date for our wedding? What on earth do you take me for? Some sort of hustling gold-digger, impatient to get you signed and sealed?'

'Hold on, babe, hold on!' He slid off the horse, the sneer on his face becoming alarm. 'I was just testing——'

'Testing?'

'I just thought you might have dropped a few hints to Daniel—okay, okay,' he soothed as she glared at him with eyes like emerald ice. 'It was just the way he came out with it. I mean, it was rather sudden, wasn't it?'

Still boiling, Lili climbed back on the rowing-machine, and started hauling away with pent-up energy. She didn't trust herself to say anything more to him just yet; the accusation had really stung. As if she were the sort of scheming minx who'd go whining to Daniel! God, didn't he know her better than that?

'Lili, I'm sorry,' he pleaded, all the starch gone out of him in the face of her indignation. 'I was teasing you, really I was. I mean, I could see it came as much of a shock to you as it did to me.'

'Yeah,' she grunted, glaring at her knees as she rowed. If she'd been in a real boat, she'd have been a mile away from him by now.

He stood uncertainly in front of her, watching her slender body exercising, a distinctly uncomfortable expression on his face. 'Come on, baby—it was only a joke.'

'Was it?' she clenched. It wasn't her idea of a joke. None of the day's events had been her idea of a joke.

'Look.' He hitched his jeans, and squatted in front of her, lowering his voice. 'I wanted to talk to you about that December business.'

'Well?' She hadn't forgiven him yet, not by a long chalk.

'Well, at least I've got my allowance back. Great, eh?'

'Great.'

'And like I said, it came as much of a shock to you as it did to me. Deciding on a date like that, just plucking it out of the air. Ridiculous. What I mean is, we don't have to go through with it, not if you don't want to.'

Lili slowly stopped rowing, letting the handles hiss back into place, and stared at him. His expression was a mixture of apprehension and hope.

'Go on,' she invited quietly, knowing in her heart what was coming.

'We've got our own lives to lead.' He tapped his chest. 'We make the decisions, baby, not Big Brother. But if he wants to think we're getting married in December, then let him. It won't do any harm in the meantime, and when the time comes, we can break it to him gently.'

'Break what to him gently?'

'That we're getting married later on. I mean,' he laughed, '*December!* It's ridiculous.'

'Is it?' She was tight-lipped, hating Martin for what he was saying, yet too tensed-up inside to protest.

'Sure it's ridiculous. I mean, I'll still be a junior driver by then. We want to wait at least another six months more.'

'Oh, Martin.' She was suddenly so empty and flat, so disgusted that she felt she was going to cry. 'I thought you meant what you said . . .'

'Just another six months, babe!'

'Another six months.' Was it relief she felt? What was this emotion that pricked at her eyes? She lifted slim fingers to wipe the tears off her lids. 'But why?'

'Look at it this way,' he said persuasively, stroking her damp hair, 'you earn a pretty good salary, right?'

'Considering what a male-orientated world it is,' she agreed evenly. 'So what?'

'So, no man likes to be earning half of what his wife earns. It would be humiliating, Lili. By this time next year I'll be earning big money, enough to support us both. That way I can feel proud, can't you see that? We could buy a fantastic house, anywhere in the world. You could stop working if you wanted to, anything.'

'The money's not that important,' she said dully.

'It is to me,' he said firmly. 'I love you, I swear I do!
Maybe I'm old-fashioned, but I want to be able to
support my wife.' He shook her, as though trying to
dislodge the sad expression on her face. 'Can't you see,
that's why Daniel dreamed the whole scene up this
afternoon!'

'I don't understand.'

'He knows me—he knows I'd want to support you
properly. By hustling us into an early marriage, he'd be
forcing me to do what he wants—join Maison Rouge,
get a steady job.'

'Are you so sure?' She looked up at him with
thoughtful green eyes.

'Why, it's obvious!' He grinned. 'He's an old fox, Lili,
but I'm getting wise to his schemes. He doesn't really
give a damn whether we marry or not. The little
charade this afternoon was just another ploy to try and
force me out of racing, using you as a lever.'

Lili dried her eyes on the handkerchief he passed her. It
did sound uneasily like one of Daniel's ideas. Sometimes
he behaved with the ruthless cunning of Machiavelli's
Prince. Could he be so heartless as to use her to try and
force Martin into the career he'd chosen for him?

As though reading her thoughts, Martin nodded.
'Don't have any illusions about Daniel,' he said quietly.
'He doesn't have a conscience. And he doesn't care how
he gets the thing he wants, as long as he gets them fast.'
He gestured around the superbly equipped gymnasium.
'How d'you think he made the money to buy this place?'
His eyes dropped to her figure, studying the curves at
her breasts and hips under the thin leotard. 'I'll tell you
one thing Daniel's right about, though,' he went on, his
voice softening. 'I reckon I should get you roped and
branded before someone else does.' He kneeled forward
to kiss her. 'Tell you what, I'll buy you that ring. How
about that?'

'How will you be able to afford it?' she asked sadly,
still wondering about Daniel. 'I don't want you to

spend all your money on a ring, Martin.'

'I'll find a way, never you mind.' He kissed her mouth. 'Mmm, you taste salty.'

'Oh, Martin.' It seemed like so long since he'd kissed her, and yet his kiss was merely a pale reminder of Daniel's masterful mouth.

'You're not going to cry any more, are you? Mustn't let Daniel see you've been crying, babe. He'll smell a rat, sure as eggs.'

'I won't cry any more.' He little knew that the tears hadn't been for him—they'd been tears of self-doubt, tears of shock at her own uncertainty.

'Good, well, I'm glad that's settled then!' He was looking quite jaunty as he stood up, his eyes bright. 'I knew you'd understand. We'll keep this as our little secret, eh? No use letting Big Brother know we've no intention of being rushed into marriage. Let him think his plan has worked!'

'Yes,' she nodded numbly.

'You're a honey.' He blew her a kiss. 'I have to rush—I'm getting a polo-lesson at five. Didn't know I was a crack horseman, did you?'

She sank down into the seat with a sigh as Martin left, whistling. Depression had settled over her like a storm-cloud. It was shameful to admit that she'd felt relief at the postponement. She felt utterly wretched, and she blamed Daniel for that, at least in part.

Yet it had also come as rather a shock to realise that Martin was planning their wedding at quite such a distance. Another year. Just how convinced were they both about this marriage, anyway?

It wasn't a question she could simply throw at Martin. He wasn't pragmatic, like her. He was an idealist . . .

She'd often thought how similar their lives had been. But there was a big difference. She'd had to work for the past four years, work hard for a living. She was used to the workaday life. Martin was not.

Although in that same four years, Martin had been drifting from one thing to another, never holding down a job, Daniel's pocket-money had enabled him to lead a luxurious, easy life. If they were to marry at this stage, he'd have to take quite a cut in his living-standard—unless she kept on working. And that raised the other problem—that he would feel humiliated if he earned so much less than she did.

Maybe it was all for the best, after all.

After all, why shouldn't Martin back out of an arrangement he'd more or less had forced on him? She couldn't blame him for that. It had been Daniel's pushing that had initiated the whole fiasco, resulting in her present hurt.

Too weary to think about it any more, she picked up her towel and went into the sauna, to lose herself in the bliss of hot steam.

CHAPTER FOUR

THURSDAY was the night of the party Daniel had organised in their honour.

Considering the distinguished guest-list, it was a surprisingly light-hearted occasion, a happy party made special by the setting. The splendid evening was warm enough for the staff to leave the windows wide open as the sun set over the hills. It was almost too warm for dancing, and most of the guests were engaged in busy discussion, only the younger ones taking the floor at the other end of the room.

Anticipating the light evening, she'd put on minimal make-up tonight, relying on a natural lip-gloss and a warm touch of eye-shadow to emphasise her natural beauty. She'd bought the shimmering black gown in Paris, and hadn't expected to wear it until she was back in England. The neckline was ultra-chaste, but the back was open in a dramatic diamond that plunged almost to her hips. It was both daring and elegant, and tonight had seemed an appropriate occasion to unveil it.

She was standing in a group with Harold Lazenby, a fascinating, if affected, man. The famous clothes designer, whose Lazenby Enterprises had recently diversified into accessories and perfumes, was wearing a pale-green suit and rather a lot of make-up, which looked incongruous on a man old enough to have white hair. As one of the high priests of modern fashion, Lili supposed, he could dress as he pleased. He was clearly impressed by her.

They'd been talking about long-range trends in fashion, and he was now describing Lili as one of the first of what he called 'a new breed of model'.

'The emphasis is on the natural,' he explained over his

71

whisky. 'Artificiality is on the way out. The advertising tycoons are looking for a healthy, youthful kind of beauty. Like Lili's, exactly. It wasn't a coincidence that *Charade* picked you for their cover, Lili.' He exhaled a plume of cigar-smoke, and smiled. 'I hope you're not going to stop modelling after you've married young Petrov. It would be a loss.'

'I don't think I'd be missed,' she said wryly, 'but you're kind to say so.'

'Oh, I mean it.' He scribbled a number on the back of a business card. 'Your agent and my art department should get together when your holiday's over,' he said in a voice meant for her ears only. 'We've always got two or three campaigns hovering. Maybe we can make something crystallise, hm? Give me a ring in Paris before you go back to the United Kingdom, won't you?'

'I will,' she promised. Wait till she told Mandy Collins she'd had an invitation from *the* Harold Lazenby!

'Now, now.' Daniel's magnificent physique was suited to perfection by the evening jacket and white tie. He had that star quality, she thought wryly, making everyone else seem shabby and plain beside him. 'Discussing business at one of my parties? I'm afraid I can't have that.'

'Don't be so mean,' Harold Lazenby pouted, the flirtatious, feminine side of his personality asserting itself immediately. With women, Lili noted amusedly, he was strictly businesslike! 'What are parties for, except to talk scandal and business?'

'You've been in the fashion game far too long,' Daniel reproved. 'Parties are for fun.'

The evening was indeed developing into merry good humour as the guests made inroads into the excellent champagne that Daniel had provided. Martin, who'd drunk more than most, was laughing heartily with a young actress by the marble fireplace. In his tuxedo and black tie he looked much more adult, more like Daniel.

She'd met almost everyone here, a remarkably cosmopolitan and varied group of people. They came from a dozen different spheres of life, yet they all had one quality—they were people who'd worked hard and gone far, people who pushed themselves to achieve great things. She let her eyes rest on Martin again. There had been a cloud over their relationship ever since that awful lunch-party on the lawn. Was he capable of the kind of effort most of the people here had made? Or did he, as Daniel had so damningly accused, seek the line of least resistance in all things?

'I'll get you grandstand tickets,' he was promising the actress. 'You must come—Le Mans is the most glamorous race of the year.'

'Are you going to win?' she cooed innocently.

'Definitely,' he said with a grin. 'We've got the best cars, the best administration——' he patted his own chest '—and the best drivers!'

Harold Lazenby turned to Daniel. 'Any chance of your taking a drive this year, Daniel?'

'I'm getting too old,' Daniel smiled, tilting his head to show the streaks of silver among the sable hair. 'It's time I started settling down.'

There was a chorus of refutation.

'You always used to dive at Le Mans,' the young actress said flirtatiously. She was probably too young to remember more than five of them, Lili thought acidly. 'Le Mans wouldn't be Le Mans without Daniel Valais in one of those bright red Porches!'

Martin snorted , rather too loudly. 'It's becoming just a business proposition to Daniel. Just advertising. Maybe he *is* getting too old.'

'Daniel will never be too old,' a woman said from a satin chaise-longue. The women all looked at him in the same way, Lili had noticed, the same adoring look in their eyes. Didn't he get sick of it? 'Besides, the older drivers are, the better.'

'And the slower,' Martin put in.

'Well,' Daniel shrugged, 'I'll consider it.'

'What about you?' Harold asked, turning shrewd eyes on to Lili. 'What do you think of Martin's career in racing?'

'I just want him to be happy,' she replied diplomatically.

'You enjoy watching him tear round a track, risking life and limb?'

'I *try* and enjoy it,' she smiled. 'It's rather magnificent, really. Crazy but magnificent.'

'I don't think it's crazy at all,' the actress fluttered up at Martin, earning herself a warm grin.

'I must confess that motor-racing has always seemed a rather eccentric sort of business proposition to me,' the surgeon beside the chaise-longue lady mused. 'I've never understood it. What's in it for Maison Rouge?'

'It's very simple. I allocate a part of the Maison Rouge advertising budget to endurance-racing each year. Instead of paying an agency to dream up glamorous images, I get one ready-made—a two hundred and thirty mile-an-hour sports-car with the company name painted across it in foot-high gold lettering. That means I get free publicity in every medium that covers motor-racing, including television, the most important of all.' He smiled, a tiger off-duty. 'I've always thought it particularly good value for money.'

'And value for money is getting very important to you, isn't it, Daniel?' Martin asked pointedly. 'More important than the sport, perhaps.' Lili winced at his attempt to provoke Daniel. Martin had drunk more than was good for him, and it had obviously made him combative.

'I can scent a little quarrel in the air,' the young actress said archly, pouting at Martin in rather the same way Harold Lazenby had pouted at Daniel. 'Do tell!'

'My cousin doesn't approve of my racing career, I'm afraid,' Martin said loudly. 'He thinks it's irresponsible. He thinks I haven't any talent.'

'But you won at Silverstone,' the actress laughed.

'Apparently that cuts no ice with Daniel!'

'Why have you put Martin in your team, then?' someone asked.

'I didn't put Martin in my team,' Daniel said calmly. 'Derek Brundle is team-boss, and he decides which drivers to employ. I have no control over things like that. After all, Derek owns the cars. I simply give him a large cheque at the beginning of the season, in exchange for which I get the cars painted in my livery—and certain other privileges.'

'So Daniel's paying my salary,' Martin pointed out with a gleeful laugh, 'whether he likes it or not. God knows it isn't much, but I bet you can hardly sleep at nights for grinding your teeth, cousin!'

'The irony hadn't escaped me,' Daniel said coolly. Lili had to look down. He could so easily have punctured Martin, humiliated him publicly. But he hadn't. 'Perhaps you'll prove me wrong at Le Mans, eh, Martin?'

'I'll have a damn good try,' Martin said with a boyish grin.

'Good.' Daniel put his glass down and turned to Lili. 'May I steal your fiancée for a dance?'

'Just don't steal her heart,' Martin smiled, his good humour evidently restored by that little outburst against his cousin. Lili let Daniel take her arm and lead her to the dance-floor.

'That was big of you,' she said in a low voice.

'What was?' he arched an eyebrow.

'Letting Matin make fun of you in public and saying nothing. It must have been a great temptation to slap him down.

'I've known Martin since he was a baby,' Daniel smiled, as though that were explanation enough. He took her in his arms. 'Am I mistaken, or have you and Martin been a little distant lately?'

'You don't miss much,' she said with a lightness she

was far from feeling. Since that meeting in the gymnasium, she and Martin had indeed been uncomfortable and tentative with one another. Her throat was suddenly dry. The contact of his hard body against her own was an unexpected shock; he felt so utterly different from Martin, so much harder and more dangerous. He didn't have the right to hold her this intimately, his male strength touching her breasts, the sensitive pit of her stomach——

'May I be intrusive and ask what it's about?'

'A storm in a teacup,' she lied. She could hardly tell him that she and Martin weren't going to marry in December after all.

Deep eyes probed hers. 'Nothing to do with your wedding plans?'

'Oh, no.' She eased away from the marshy subject. 'Do you think Martin really does have a chance of doing well at Le Mans?'

'If he keeps his head. I must admit that he seems a little more mature these days. Perhaps your influence over him is changing him for the better.'

'You mean you've changed your opinion?' she asked in mock-disbelief.

'Martin has a lot of growing up to do,' he said indirectly.

'And me? Have I got a lot of growing up to do as well?'

'You have something Martin lacks, chérie. You know that as well as I do.' He met her eyes with a slow smile. 'It's too warm in here. Shall we go out to the balcony?'

The evening air was deliciously cool on her bare shoulders. By the way Daniel had been looking at her tonight, the Paris dress suited her tanned skin and blonde hair well, and she was glad to be looking at her best. But she was tense, too, just beneath her composure.

They were private here, the curtain at the open doorway stirring gently in the breeze. The dance had just ended, but he didn't let her go. Instead, he waited for the next number, a slow, explicitly sexy song that was a current world-wide hit.

'Loosen up. It's like dancing with a statue,' he complained, voice warm against her cheek.

'I'll try,' she muttered. She dropped her shoulders and exhaled slowly, a trick a photographer had taught her of inducing relaxation.

The moon had risen high and pearly in the velvet-blue sky as they danced on the black and white marble flags of the terrace, in a private, almost mystical world of their own.

'So you think racing is crazy,' he smiled. 'But isn't the modelling world just as crazy?'

'In a different way.' Her heart was beating faster than she liked, and she was alarmed by the thought that he would be able to feel it against his chest, and realise how much he affected her. 'Except people don't kill themselves modelling!'

'You're worried about Martin?'

'Of course I am,' she retorted. 'I would be silly if I wasn't.'

'But not worried enough to talk some sense into his thick head?' He laid a warm finger on her lips to silence her. 'Very well, I promise I won't mention it again. Let's talk about you instead. Harold was dying to meet you, you know. He saw your face on the *Charade* cover, of course, but he was very impressed with the *Cosmopolitan* shots.'

'Oh, those again!' A memory of her provocative near-nakedness in those pictures crossed her thoughts. A flash of sheer devilry made her ask innocently, 'What did *you* think of them?'

For the first time, there was a glint of something, deep in his eyes. 'As a lady shortly about to be married to another man, I don't think you want to know.'

'Oh, come on!' The teasing words slipped out before she had time to think. 'I want to hear what you saw in them.'

'Very well.' His hands drifted up her back, tracing her spine in a way that made her skin shiver with sudden goosebumps. 'I saw the most attractive woman I've ever seen.' His voice was husky, the sound of soft wood torn by the saw. 'A woman with the face of an angel. A woman whose body was straight out of my dreams, silky and slender and the colour of poured gold. Eyes as clear as mountain water, and a mouth both sinful and innocent. A woman made for love, a woman who compelled my desire. Shall I tell you any more?'

'No.' She could hardly say the word, her mouth was so paper-dry.

His laughter was velvety. 'Have I disturbed you, *chérie*? You should be used to men desiring you by now.'

'I think we should go and sit down now,' she said in an uneven voice. She'd been able to dance with him until two minutes ago without really thinking about it. Now his touch was like flame against her skin. Now she knew she would never be able to look into those grey eyes again, without remembering what he'd said tonight.

'And I think we should stay a while,' he countered imperturbably. His hands moved to her waist, assessing the slender grace of her body. 'You did ask, you know.'

'I shouldn't have,' she said tersely, almost to herself. 'And you shouldn't have said that. Not if you're really Martin's friend.'

'You confuse desire with execution,' he said, eyes amused now. 'Just because I want you doesn't mean that I intend to have you.'

'There's not the slightest chance of that, anyhow!' she snapped at him, blood surging angrily to her cheeks.

'Of course there isn't. You love Martin. You're going to marry him . . .' he was wickedly expert at that ironic pause '. . . in December.'

Martin. She twisted to look at the doorway, but the

curtain was still concealing them from the other guests. Martin ... It terrified her how young and irrelevant Daniel made Martin seem. In Daniel's arms, right now, it was as though she'd never met Martin Petrov, had never agreed to become his wife. Terrifying, and yet there was nothing she could do about it.

'Relax, Lili.' He was using the sensuous dance as an excuse to knead the tense muscles at the side of her neck. 'You're getting upset about nothing.'

'I'm not upset!' The catch in her voice made a nonsense of that statement.

'Good.' The massaging fingers were wickedly expert, tracing the tendons in her stiff neck, the tops of her shoulders, beginning to spread delicious relaxation right through her body. 'Let's just dance, then. We won't talk unless you want to.'

His touch had some dark magic in it, melting her resistance from within like strong wine. As his fingers eased the knots out of her shoulders, his body was close against hers, brushing against her breasts and thighs provocatively, making her senses swim.

Unable to help herself, she let her head droop against his shoulder, her cheek resting on the warm plane of his chest, her hair in golden disarray. He cradled her tenderly, swaying her to the slow, insistent beat.

When the song ended, she didn't suggest they return to the party. She simply stayed in Daniel's arms, surrendering to the power she had no way of fighting against. It was like a dream, and yet real, more real than anything in her life before. The next song was equally slow, equally sensuous, and she was moving against him again, their bodies fluid, as one.

It was happening again, that trick of the twilight that put her under his spell.

She was barely aware of Daniel's fingers spreading to cup her face, tilting her mouth to his as naturally as though they'd done this a thousand times before.

It was a kiss that held perfection, his strength

invading the moist softness of her surrender with devastating fulness. She clung to him, arms around his neck in shameless abandon, her mind only aware of Daniel, the need for her she could feel in his body and in his kiss.

'You taste of champagne this time,' he whispered. 'God, you're so beautiful, Lili . . .' She was too stunned to think of resisting as he kissed her again, this time harder, more demanding, so that she moaned against his mouth, her body melting against his, offering him her aroused breasts, the hunger in her hips.

This was what she'd been aching for, dying for. This one-ness with Daniel. It all seemed to crystallise in this kiss. As she responded to him, twining her arms around his neck, her thighs pressed to the hardness of his desire, a part of her mind was aware that nothing else would ever be as perfect as this. It wasn't just a kiss, a caress between a woman and a sensual man. It was something that altered her whole universe, fulfilled her in a way she'd only dreamed of.

His body was unbelievably strong, the muscles under her restless hands iron-hard, dominant. She whimpered helplessly as his hand brushed her taut flanks, rising to cup her breast, finding her erect nipple under the thin material.

The end of the song brought a little sanity back to Lili's melting emotions. If Martin was watching them——

She struggled free of him, her breath ragged in her pulsing throat. 'Please,' she begged in the dim light, 'Martin will see us!'

'He's not watching.' There was a glow in the grey eyes like clouds before a storm. 'He's too busy with Marisa Legrange. And you weren't thinking of Martin a minute ago. What does that tell you?'

'Was this your idea of a test?' she asked him shakily, unable to believe quite how easily she'd succumbed to his so-potent attraction. 'Trying to see how loyal I am to him?'

'Maybe.' His eyes were still focused on her mouth. 'Maybe I just wanted you.' He kissed her again, his mouth ruthlessly hard, making her gasp. 'Would you be unfaithful to him?' he asked silkily. 'If I asked you?'

'Please take me back inside,' she asked him unsteadily. Her knees were shaking, her heart pounding in her throat. '*Please*,' she whispered as he was about to speak again. 'I can't bear any more!'

His eyes searched hers, then, as though seeing how tautly she was stretched, he nodded. 'You'll answer that question. One day.'

She felt physically drained as he escorted her back into the brightly lit room. It hardly seemed to matter that if any of the guests had seen him kiss her like that there was going to be a most terrible scandal.

But it didn't seem that any of the party had noticed that intensely passionate kiss.

She let out a shaky breath as she joined Martin by the mantelpiece, Martin smiling as he took her hand.

'Well,' he challenged, 'you've been out there a long time! Is the Daniel charm as potent as they say it is?'

'I didn't notice,' she said, trying to sound easy. 'It's a splendid evening.' But Daniel's eyes were on her, ironic and very male, and she felt the colour rise to her cheeks.

'You're a lucky dog,' Daniel told Martin gently. 'She's as light as a feather in a man's arms.'

'Someone said the same thing about *me* last week,' the actress said poutingly. She held up appealing arms to Daniel. 'Care to take me for a dance, *beau monsieur*?'

'With the greatest of pleasure,' Daniel purred, towering over the diminutive, feminine creature. Lili watched them go, feeling the tension in her give way to dull depression. How could he so easily take another woman's body in his arms—after what he'd just been doing to her? The thought that he could transfer that desire to someone else was a stab of torment. She watched Marisa Legrange's body moulding against his, and felt sick. Were Daniel's reactions to her even a tenth as potent as hers to him?

Martin was telling a joke she'd heard twice before, and she dragged a laugh out of herself, taking his arm and holding it close to her, as though for comfort. She ought to be concentrating on bridging the distance that had developed between her and her fiancé. Beside what she was going through with Daniel, though, it hardly seemed important any more.

The party was still lively by one in the morning when the first guests started to leave. It wasn't till nearly two that Lili was saying good night to Martin in the great hall.

He leaned forward to kiss her, and Lili closed her eyes. She wanted so badly to feel the old magic, but somehow she couldn't. It wasn't there. She held him close, hating herself for her hypocrisy, for the betrayal that was now inside her.

Why couldn't Martin's kiss do to her what Daniel's did? Why was it only a colourless copy? People who said love was blind were wrong. Love was sharp-eyed, capriciously cruel, a wicked boy who loved to pull the wings from butterflies.

'I wish I were coming to bed with you,' he growled, his breath wine-laden against her neck. 'You know how much I want you, Lili. I could make you so happy. Why are you such a little puritan about sex?'

'I won't be when we're married.' It came out automatically by now, she'd said it so often. Maybe it disturbed her that she desired Martin so little lately. It had been such a passion at first. Maybe it was something to do with her cycle. Maybe it was the summer, the country air, the upset over the wedding. Maybe she simply had a weak sex-drive. Some women did.

But Daniel had proved otherwise with one kiss tonight. She hugged Martin, wishing to heaven there were some red-hot iron of the mind that could sear out Daniel's image for ever.

'When we're married. You expect me to wait twelve months?'

'It would only have been six months,' she pointed out with a glimmer of a smile.

'Very funny.' His expression was dangerous. 'You aren't the only woman in the world, you know, Lili.'

'No,' she said, painfully hurt by the implication. 'But I'm the one you've asked to be your wife.'

'Oh, baby.' He held her close. 'I'm sorry, I don't know what made me say that. You know I'd never——'

'We'll make love,' she promised him in a whisper. They didn't have much choice any more. She'd once thought it would be a mere few months till their wedding, that it would have been easy to wait that short period. But Martin was right—a year was too long, far too long, to wait for sex.

Maybe that was the answer, after all. To give herself to Martin, let him obliterate Daniel's image with his lovemaking. Maybe if she gave Martin her virginity, that would bind her to him for ever, the way she so desperately wanted it to be. It was supposed to be a mystical thing, wasn't it?

'We will make love, I promise. Just not here, not at L'Hermitage.'

'Where, then?' he wanted to know.

'Back in London, maybe. Now go and get your sleep,' she commanded him, pulling away abruptly with every nerve in her body prickling. 'You're going to be racing in a week's time.'

'Is anything wrong?' he asked, peering at her in concern.

'Nothing. Nothing.' She clung to him, her eyes seeing only Daniel.

'If you'd let me make love to you,' he said in a low voice, 'I could make everything so much better.'

Bonsoir Mam'selle, bonsoir M'sieu Martin.' Louis the butler was locking the doors and windows, and it was obvious they weren't going to have any more privacy. Martin turned away in sullen irritation at the interruption.

'I just wanted to make thing up,' he said tightly.
'You're still upset with me about that ridiculous
wedding business, aren't you?'

'I promise I'm not!'

'Then Daniel's been getting to you.'

'I don't know what you mean by "getting to me",'
she said unhappily.

'I mean you've been spending a lot of time with him,'
Martin said grimly. 'Time which he's no doubt put to
good use. What horror stories about me has he been
filling your ears with now?'

'He hasn't told me any horror stories about you, as a
matter of fact.'

His eyes, sometimes so like Daniel's, searched hers. 'I
find that hard to believe.'

'Why should you?' she asked. 'Unless there *are* things
in your life you'd rather I didn't know about?'

'So he *has* been poisoning you against me!'

'Oh, Martin.' She was too emotionally upset, too
tired to wrangle with him now. 'You're being so unfair.'

The catch in her voice made his scowl disappear. 'I'm
sorry, love, so sorry.' Once again he was cradling her in
his arms contritely. 'I'm getting over-tense, I guess. It's
Le Mans coming up. It gets to me.'

'I know.' She kissed him wearily. 'We'll talk about it
tomorrow,' she sighed. 'I'm sorry, but I'm just so tired.'

'Go to bed.' He gave her a gentle push in the
direction of the stairs. 'Good night, my love.'

As she walked slowly through the magnificent house
to her bedroom, she told herself that the feeling would
pass. It *had* to, because she couldn't go on like this for
much longer.

Maybe Martin was right. Maybe they should have
made love as soon as they'd fallen in love, the way so
many modern couples seemed to do.

If he'd seen her kissing Daniel tonight——

The thoughts chased each other restlessly through her
brain, not letting her settle.

Her room was airy, the curtains billowing softly in the breeze, reminding her once again of that first night here.

She leaned on the sill, staring out over the moonlit garden, the glinting, mysterious hills beyond.

She had to rationalise her feelings. Tonight had been an aberration, it was important to understand that. An accident, a kink in the flow of her life resulting from all sorts of hidden tensions she couldn't really explain. After Le Mans, she and Martin could go away together again, somewhere miles and miles away from Daniel Valais.

Lili closed her eyes with a sigh. She'd thought she had more self-control. More discipline.

Discipline was something she'd needed to have these past five years. She'd never felt strange, growing up without parents. Perhaps that was a tribute to Auntie Joan's loving kindness. All she remembered of her parents, though, was a vague presence, a dim image that might just as easily have been a dream.

She knew that her father had been an architect, her mother a noted society beauty. But she'd been just two years old when they'd died in a light aeroplane belonging to her Uncle Ted. She'd been in the flying-club lounge, asleep in the lap of a family friend. They'd thought the short pleasure-flight might make her airsick, so she hadn't been on board when the engine had failed a second after take-off. But on that summer's day, her mother and father had both died on the tarmac beside the wreckage before ambulances could arrive.

She remembered nothing about that August afternoon.

Her mother's sister, Joan Lucas, had become her foster-mother. Joan, librarian of the tiny local library, had never married. Looking back, after Joan's death, Lili had realised that she herself might have been one of the reasons for that. But in any case, Joan was as plain as her sister had been lovely, and there had been no queue of eligible men knocking at the door of 37 Maybury Avenue.

At twelve, Lili had started at an exclusive boarding-school in Kent, according to her mother's wishes as expressed in her will and during her lifetime. There had been just enough money in her parents' estate to pay the fees—it had been Joan Lucas who'd painstakingly sewn the expensive grey school uniforms. Dresses and blouses and gymslips and hockey skirts . . .

Odd schooldays. The only real difference Lili had noticed between herself and other girls, despite the fact that they were all far wealthier than she, was that she was quieter, more determined to succeed. Even then, she'd been learning the vital importance of relying on yourself.

Cancer had killed Joan when Lili was seventeen. She'd left Lili everything she had, which hadn't been much. And she'd left an aching hole in Lili's life.

Lili had gone straight out to work. A record-shop for eighteen months. She'd been training for a managership when the parent company had gone bust, leaving her redundant. Then the High Fliers kite-factory in Tunbridge Wells. An eccentric job by anyone's standards. Long afternoons on the downs, hauling the gaily coloured things high into the sky, bringing them back for aerodynamic analysis. That had been fun, but it simply hadn't paid well enough to keep body and soul together.

At her third job, in the fashion boutique, she'd got her first inkling that her beauty and grace could work for her. The shop was always full of fashion people, models, agents, photographers. It had been Jerry Momsworth who'd stopped one day, asked her to model some earrings. The shots were good, her elegant profile flattering the flashy jewels.

He'd passed her name on to his friends, who'd found something exciting in her face, the way she moved. It hadn't so much snowballed as drifted along. Until the modelling jobs had started cutting into her proper work time.

She'd learned she could rely on her looks. In a sense, working with her face; her body, had been the ultimate self-reliance. Like Martin, working with his body in the cockpit of a sports-car. Yes, fire or acid or sharp steel could end your career in three seconds; but Lili had enough courage to face that possibility without flinching.

Did the thought of Martin crashing frighten her? Frankly, it terrified her. Every time he got into a racing-car her nerves stayed on edge until she saw him getting out again. But she recognised so clearly what racing represented to Martin. A way out. A way out of mediocrity, nonentity, the grey monotony of everyday life. Yes, Daniel had probably been right; Martin wasn't blessed with the multitude of talents his cousin possessed. But sports-car racing, dangerous and gruelling as it was, at least offered him a chance to excel.

Exactly the way modelling had done for her. Modelling had offered her a way out, too, a way out and up, into the sun that had so long eluded her!

Tiredly, she turned, drew the curtain, and prepared for bed. Why had the idea of marriage and children tarnished? Maybe beneath all her disappointment over the December business, she was actually reluctant to settle down and lose her liberty just yet. She'd thought of Martin once as the sunshine she'd been looking for all her life. She'd thought it would be easy to give up her newly found career for him.

From the way Harold Lazenby had been talking, he was meditating offering her a commission of some kind. If it was her career which really interested her, then why couldn't she whip up the excitement she ought to feel about *that*? After all, meeting Lazenby might be the most important thing that had happened to her since *Charade*.

Naked, she studied her body in the floor-to-ceiling mirror. A beautiful body, taut and slender, blessed with an inner grace. The breasts were perhaps too full; one photographer had complained, 'They're marvellous, darling, but they stretch the lines of that blouse so. Can't you *do* something with them?'

She smiled at the memory, touching the full curves with delicate fingertips. The raised, coral-pink centres made her think inconsequentially of Daniel. She let her eyes run down the reflection of her flat belly, the flare of her hips, the perfect line of her long, slim thighs, trying to see herself through his eyes. She couldn't do it. Maybe she simply wasn't vain enough.

Had he really desired her? Or had what he'd said and done tonight been a game, the deliberate mockery of a potently sexual man? She'd probably never know.

Thinking of him had brought goose-flesh rising on her forearms, her nipples tensing with a life of their own. She pulled on her nightie and slid between the cool sheets, switching off the bedside lamp. He was changing her life more surely than Martin had ever done.

Martin *was* her sunshine. He had to be. He was her fiancé. She couldn't afford to let Daniel influence or affect her any further, no matter how important he was in their lives. Anyone who made her distrust her own feelings for Martin—and that was exactly what Daniel did—was dangerous.

Danger without reward. Because she could never have him, no matter how deeply involved with him she became.

CHAPTER FIVE

LILI knew in her heart that things could never be the same between her and Daniel again.

It wasn't just that he'd told her he desired her, though that in itself would have been disturbing enough.

It was the suggestion he'd left hanging in the air that they could have a love-affair. A relationship quite independent of her engagement to Martin.

Coming from any other man, she'd have known how to handle it. Coming from Daniel, it made her tremble, terrified her with her own weakness. He'd just been playing with her. If ever he really wanted her, would she have the power to resist?

Even if she'd been totally immoral about it, she felt she didn't have the strength to face a love-affair with a man as dangerous as Daniel. Dangerous emotionally, that was. If he once possessed her, she suspected she'd be his always, helplessly. No man, not even Martin, could come close to what he did to her. And that, too opened up a whole new area of ambiguity and doubt.

She tried her best to avoid him over Friday and the weekend. She'd even managed to avoid eating with him, pleading a diet, and fixing herself a private sandwich in the vast kitchens, under the perplexed eye of a chef who'd been diligently preparing dishes like *gratin de langouste aux épinards* and *confit de canard* in her honour.

On Monday, though, preparations for the twenty-four-hour race at Le Mans had already begun, and there was a great deal going on to distract her from her troubles.

The two dozen or more teams were beginning to

assemble at Le Mans, intent on preparing their cars and
drivers for the biggest and most prestigious race of the
season in a week's time. The race was due to begin on
Saturday afternoon, at three o'clock. It would last
exactly twenty-four hours, going through the night on
headlights, to end on Sunday afternoon at three.

The Maison Rouge outfit, as serious contenders, were
among the first arrivals. Daniel and Martin both
wanted to be at the track in the afternoon, and so the
three of them flew the twenty miles to Le Mans in one
of the helicopters.

The atmosphere of tension that was building up had
already started affecting Lili, making her restless and
uneasy. She was completely silent during the helicopter
journey to the race-track, her mind brooding. Martin,
too, had been unusually preoccupied, his normally
handsome face creased with thought. Only Daniel
seemed indifferent to the mood, piloting the machine
with calm proficiency.

It was another perfect evening, the heat of
midsummer making itself felt.

Not for the first time, Lili was reflecting that Daniel's
attitude towards racing was oddly ambiguous. On the
one hand it obviously fascinated him—witness the fact
that he occasionally took a drive in one of the cars
himself, the fact that he'd chosen endurance-racing as
an advertising medium in the first place. On the other,
there was a wariness in him towards racing.

Partly, she guessed, he would never forget that his
mother had died at the wheel of a sports-car. Partly, too,
he must recognise that racing appealed to the darker side
of his nature. The aggressive, almost primitive force that
lay just beneath his sophisticated veneer of civilisation.
Maybe he recognised that, and kept it under tight control.

Maybe, too, that was what set him so against Martin
taking part. Maybe he was all too aware of the
terrifying energies that the sport could unleash in both
machines and men.

Yet she believed that Martin really did have that essential talent, after all. And if, as she was prepared to admit, Martin's character did err on the casual side, wouldn't it be far better for him to do something he was really committed to? She'd never fooled herself about the dangers; yet she recognised that Martin was the sort of man who needed to do what he was really cut out for.

The track, bathed in brilliant sunshine, presented a very different picture from the last occasion she'd flown over it, on her way to L'Hermitage for the first time.

'Look at the crowds,' Martin said, almost in awe. Five days before the start of the world's most famous race, the paddock was already jammed with people and cars. 'Not even Silverstone was like this before the race.'

As Daniel landed the helicopter near the main car-park, a steady stream of human and mechanical traffic was pouring through the compound gates to the vast complex of trailers, caravans and mobile homes that constituted the 'village', the hub of the circuit.

Derek Brundle was on hand to greet them as the chopper settled down beside the track, trees lashing wildly in the gale from its rotors. Derek, looking immaculate as usual despite the afternoon heat, and in dark glasses as always, was clearly delighted to see Daniel. He was one of the Maison Rouge team she'd already met, in England, during the preparations for the Silverstone 1000. Derek had once been a racing-driver; now middle-aged, and having made himself a wealthy man selling his own tractors, he was one of the most respected team-managers in endurance-racing.

'My warmest congratulations on your engagement,' he said to Lili once he'd exchanged a handshake with Daniel. 'I hope you'll both be very happy. You look wonderful, Lili. *Ça va*, Martin? Feeling fit?'

'Never better.' Martin shook hands, and Derek drove them in the big Mercedes through the compound to the pits garages.

There were at least thirty cars standing in the crowded pits, but it was easy to distinguish the two crimson and gold Porsches at the far end, surrounded by mechanics in red Maison Rouge overalls.

'How are things going?' Daniel wanted to know.

'Some good, some bad,' Derek told him. 'The hotel we've got this year is appalling. Bruno's sciatica is playing up again—you'll hear more of that later. And we blew an engine today, testing the cars. Another expensive kiss-off.'

Daniel smiled at the catalogue of woe. 'I'll let you all stay at L'Hermitage next time. What will a rebuild on the engine cost?'

'Name a figure, then double it. A hundred and twenty thousand francs, something like that.'

Daniel gave Lili a dry look. 'It's an expensive business financing this lot,' he commented, and she nodded in awe. Daniel took her arm, as though he couldn't bear not to be touching her all the time. Why couldn't Martin be more positive? It was always Daniel whose hard body was beside hers, as though he deliberately edged Martin out.

'*Tiens!* The love-birds are back in circulation.' A small, dark man in white overalls swatted Martin happily on the shoulder as they arrived. '*Félicitations*, Martin.'

'*Merci*, Jacques.'

'You haven't forgotten how to drive, eh? The cars are going damned well, *mon vieux*. They'll blow your socks off. Think you can hang on to the wheel for long enough to win?'

Smiling, Martin introduced him to Lili. 'Jacques Davel, chief mechanic. If we win the championship this year, he'll be claiming all the credit.'

'*Naturellement*,' the little man agreed. He had bright, humorous eyes which were sizing Lili's figure up in a very Gallic way. 'Daniel and Derek give the orders, but I'm the one who keeps this whole immoderate show on the road. Delighted to make your acquaintance, Mam'selle Bergman. Martin has been a lucky devil, as always. You are even lovelier than your photographs.'

'Lili, please,' she corrected him with a smile. Davel was someone she'd taken to at once. 'And I'm glad your cars are going well.'

'We might even win. If your fiancé can stay out of the trees,' he added, then roared with laughter at her expression. Another Fuji joke. Maybe racing people laughed at death to keep it at bay?

Lili shook hands with Christian Seberg and Bruno Weissman, the team's two senior drivers. They were similar types, she thought, hard-bitten and experienced, men who would be reliable in any emergency. She measured Martin against their seasoned self-assurance. Was he really cut from the same cloth as these two warriors? Certainly, none of the team treated Martin in any way differently. As far as appearances went, he was a junior driver, no more and no less.

'Congratulations, Miss Bergman.' Bruno, taller and better looking, had met her once before. 'I hope you and Martin will be very happy.'

'That goes for me, too.' Cool and beautiful, Sabrina Hobbs was Derek Brundle's right-hand woman, employed to keep a watchful eye on administration and make sure everything ran smoothly around the drivers. They'd met before, in England. Lili thanked her, accepting the handshake. It was good to meet another woman in this very male world.

As usual, Sabrina was in black; sleekly tight trousers and open-necked blouse, the Maison Rouge name picked out in gold thread over the delicate peaks of her breasts. She gave Lili's very English grey suit and silk blouse a quick, admiring once-over, then offered champagne. 'Would you like some *Première Cuvée*? It seems appropriate.'

'Christian was testing the number-one car just before you came,' Derek Brundle said, sipping champagne, 'and it really *is* quick, Daniel.' He drew on a Balkan Sobranie, then slicked his fair hair over his bald patch, exhaling smoke smoothly. 'If nothing goes wrong, he might take the lap record at Le Mans.'

'So might I,' Martin put in, a shade resentfully. Lili felt sorry for him—he was very much the cub in this company of lions, oversensitive to any imagined slight. 'You never know!'

'I do know,' Derek said drily. 'One day, maybe. But you're not going to take any lap records just yet, old son. You've got a lot more practising to do before you're as quick as Christian.'

There was good-humoured laughter at Martin's expense as they walked over to the Porsche.

Lili stared at the car, more fully aware of its presence than ever before. It was a predatory-looking beast, crouching squatly on massive wheels, the curved headlamp covers and raked windscreen heightening the impression of hurtling speed. The bodywork was immaculately finished, the long, sweeping bonnet glittering scarlet and gold with the Maison Rouge logo.

'This is the number one car.' Daniel slapped it casually on the bonnet, making the fibreglass ring.

Printed on the door were the names of the three drivers. Followed by their blood-group symbols.

Her involuntary grimace didn't escape Daniel's eye. 'FISA regulations,' he smiled, showing perfect white teeth. 'Drivers occasionally need blood.'

'I'm aware of that, Daniel.' She sounded too poised, too cool, but he didn't appear to notice.

'The cars are Porsche 962s,' Derek said proudly. 'They develop around seven hundred brake horse-power at peak revs.'

'I don't think Lili knows what you're talking about,' Daniel said gently. His deep grey eyes held hers. 'For one thing it means top speeds of well over two hundred miles an hour. More like two hundred and thirty down the Mulsanne straight. At that speed, everything in the world is just a blur except for a tiny little patch directly in front of the driver.'

'That's the old war-horse talking.' Derek Brundle laid a hand on Daniel's broad shoulder. 'Well, my friend, are you going to be driving at Le Mans this time?'

'Everyone seems to have that question on their lips,' Daniel sighed.

'It's not a question,' Derek said calmly. 'It's an invitation.'

Grey eyes flicked at him. 'I see.'

'The car has never gone better than this, Daniel. Those aerodynamic changes we made after Silverstone are really making a big difference. We've got a chance of winning this year.' He paused. 'Bruno?'

'I do not think I shall be fit for the race,' Bruno Weissman said in his deep voice.

'You've seen Graham?' Daniel asked sharply. Weissman nodded.

'I saw him today. Dr Prince agrees with me that I should not drive.' He raised his arms, obviously with pain. 'I'm stiff, Monsieur Valais. A stiff driver is a dangerous driver.'

'Martin's not ready to take a full share in the car,' Derek said firmly. Martin's expression was of barely disguised disgust. Lili glanced from his displeasure to Daniel's face, trying to read the expression behind that beautiful bronze mask. 'We could hire in another driver, of course. One of the Formula One people, maybe, like Johanssen. He's driven for us before. Or you could take Bruno's place yourself. You and Le Mans are a good combination, Daniel, that's important. We'd have a real chance of winning for the fourth time.'

'Flattery will get you nowhere,' Daniel smiled. 'I'm thirty-four, Derek. Even Martin thinks I'm too old. Maybe you should ring Eric Johanssen.'

'Take number one for a spin,' was Derek's only reply. 'We've got it kitted out with a lightweight passenger seat, so that Jacques could go round with Christian.'

'Indeed.' He glanced at Lili with glinting grey eyes. 'I'll take Lili with me, in that case.'

'Hold on!' she protested hastily. She'd been so absorbed by the exchange that she'd almost missed that little notion. 'I'm not sure I want to get into a racing-car, not even with Daniel!'

'If you're going to marry a racing-driver,' Derek chuckled, 'you'd better start learning about racing-cars fairly quickly! Sabrina, get one of Christian's helmets—they ought to fit Lili.'

Martin was standing silent and expressionless. The mechanics were already preparing the engine, filling the tank with the spiralling tube of the safety apparatus. Derek leaned forward and swung the lightweight door open. 'Just get in,' he invited persuasively. 'Try it out for size. Going round the track at Le Mans is not an experience that comes along every day, I promise you!'

Lili hesitated, more nervous than ever. This was a challenge she had to either accept or turn her back on. She met Daniel's eyes. They were smiling wickedly, as though waiting for her to chicken out. Tightening the stormy line of her mouth, she stepped past him and lowered herself gingerly into the seat.

'Ouff!' It was unexpectedly hard, hugging her hips and thighs, and so low that her legs were stretched almost straight out in front of her. The windscreen raked inches away from her eyes, the instruments curving in an arc around the driver's seat beside her. A claustrophobic world of steel and black vinyl that smelled of oil and sweat.

The car was so low that the people round it towered like giants. Most of the mechanics were grinning broadly, that we-know-something-you-don't expression that was hardly reassuring!

Daniel buckled the safety-harness across her shoulders and lap, pulling it painfully tight, so that she was immobile to all intents and purposes. 'Can you breathe?' he asked.

To Susan Welland
Mills & Boon
FREEPOST
PO Box 236
Croydon
Surrey
CR9 9EL

SEND NO MONEY NOW!

Free Books Certificate

Dear Susan,

Please send me my 4 FREE Temptations together with my Mills & Boon Tote Bag. Please also reserve a special Reader Service Subscription for me. If I decide to subscribe, I shall receive 6 superb new titles every two months for just £7.20*, post and packing free. If I decide not to subscribe, I shall write to you within 10 days. The free books and Tote Bag will be mine to keep in any case.

I understand that I am under no obligation whatsoever — I can cancel or suspend my subscription at any time simply by writing to you. I am over 18 years of age.

Your exclusive FREE
Mills & Boon Tote Bag

_____ Signature _____

Name: _____
(BLOCK CAPITALS PLEASE)
Address: _____

_____ Postcode _____

8A6TEB

TEMPTATION

Beautiful sensual novels to hold you irresistibly captive

Take 4 exciting titles as your free introductory gift from Mills & Boon Reader Service.

Temptation novels bring you all the joy and tenderness of age-old romance as it is experienced in contemporary love affairs.

And to introduce you to this powerful, highly-charged series, we'll send you 4 Temptation titles and an exclusive Mills & Boon Tote Bag, absolutely FREE when you complete and return this card.

We'll also reserve a subscription for you to the Mills & Boon Reader Service, which means you'll enjoy:

★ SIX WONDERFUL NOVELS — sent direct to you every two months.

★ FREE POSTAGE & PACKING — we pay all the extras.

★ FREE REGULAR NEWSLETTER — packed with competitions, author news and much more

★ SPECIAL OFFERS — selected exclusively for our readers.

There's no obligation or commitment — you can cancel your subscription at any time. Simply complete and return this card today to receive your free introductory gifts. No Stamp is required.

TEMPTATION
This Time, This Moment
MARION SMITH COLLINS

TEMPTATION
A Gift of Wild Flowers
GEORGIA BOCKOVEN

TEMPTATION
ow the Game is Played
MARY CANON

TEMPTATION
Collaboration
LASS SMALL

'Just,' she said in a breathless voice.

'Must be too loose,' he smiled, and pulled the straps an impossible notch tighter. Then he slid into the seat beside her, his lithe body fitting the cockpit like a hand into a Florentine leather glove. 'All right?'

'It isn't very comfortable.' Her voice sounded small, almost frightened. She had to remind herself that she was an independent woman, matured and hardened by a competitive career and a hard life!

'Dr Porsche doesn't build them for comfort.' Daniel strapped himself in, and pressed a red button on the console. There was a heavy churning sound just behind her for a second, and then the engine burst into shattering life.

A rasping, frightening roar, powerful enough to shiver the whole lightweight shell like a dried leaf. Needles were trembling in the dashboard, the vibration surging up her spine and filling her chest.

Conversation was impossible. The gaping mouths of the twin exhausts were inches away from her seat, spewing that savage sound out in a haze of engine fumes. God, what must fifty of these monsters sound like, revving up on the starting-grid?

Jacques Davel offered her the full-face helmet, and she pulled it on, strapping it under her chin. The padded interior gripped her cheeks and temples, muffling the worst of the engine noise. The door thumped shut, imprisoning her in this tight, harsh, constricting little womb of a world.

Someone gave a thumbs up in front of the screen, and the Porsche was surging forward under Daniel's sure hands, rumbling and bumping its way on to the track.

'Don't worry.' She jumped as Daniel's voice crackled in her earphones. 'I'll bring you back in one piece!'

Then a giant hand was pushing her remorselessly back into her seat, crushing the breath from her lungs. The track ahead had begun to ribbon under the car, the

grandstands and trees moving past with an acceleration
that seemed to go on and on and on, until they were little
more than a coloured blur at the edges of her vision.

At the first bend she knew why they were both
strapped so tightly to the bucket seats. The cornering
force was terrifying, dragging at her body like invisible
claws. Then on to the straight, and a giant push in the
back as the car accelerated with unbelievable power.

She'd never been driven this fast in her life before.
This was a howling world so far removed from
everyday reality as to be devastating. Utter terror was
rising in her, irrational and mindless. Numbly, she was
aware of Daniel's brown hand snaking the gearstick
through the gate, the answering howl of the engine, the
quivering of the chassis beneath her.

'Oh, God,' she whispered, inaudible to anything but
her own mind. The next bend was hurtling towards
them so terribly quickly!

'Did I tell you,' his voice crackled conversationally in
her headphones, 'how beautiful you look today?'

'Daniel!' He'd miscalculated the bend, had forgotten
to brake, in a second they'd be exploding into the
scenery, mangled and smashed——

The brakes were a gigantic hawser that hauled their
speed down, the harness biting into her shoulders as
though the nylon webbing had become a steel trap.

Again that awful swing, worse than any fairground
horror she'd experienced as a child, then another brief
straight, then the chicane—the sequence of S-bends that
forced Daniel to slow the missile down as they scissored
through, the tyres thudding over the striped corruga-
tions at the very edge of the track. For a moment the
world was almost normal again, the dizzying blur
resolving into steel barriers, green trees beyond, and a
clear sky. She dragged her head sideways to look at the
speedometer. It was reading almost a hundred miles an
hour, and even as she watched, the red needle had
begun to arc round the black dial again, past 150, 160.

Her head was forced backwards again. The tarmac was hurtling by, inches beneath them. She suppressed an insane desire to giggle. The terror was almost fun, once you'd learned to trust Daniel. After the long bend that seemed to plaster her insides firmly against her right-hand ribs, they were on the straight. The pits were hurtling towards them. She caught a split-second glimpse of Martin, one hand raised, before he dissolved into a pale blur.

The deep voice was in her earphones again. 'Okay?'

'I think—think so.' Her body was shivering, though, and she still had that insane desire to giggle. Then they were going round again.

The second lap was even faster.

When Daniel finally drove the car into the pit-area, and switched the engine off, her ears were still ringing. Her legs were so wobbly as Martin helped her out of the cockpit that she had to lean on the bonnet to get her helmet off and shake her blonde hair loose.

'Enjoy yourself?' Derek grinned.

'Good God,' was all she could say. She looked at Martin. 'You want to do that for *fun*?'

'For a living, not for fun.' He smiled rather tensely. He was obviously not over-pleased.

'I hope I didn't scare you?' Daniel said gently, unbuckling his helmet.

'You terrified me,' she admitted, green eyes sparkling at him. The excitement of the ride seemed to have shattered the self-conscious barrier between her and Daniel. 'But I loved it!' Impulsively, she leaned over to kiss his tanned cheek. She turned to catch Martin sending Daniel a resentful glance.

Martin was jealous, she realised suddenly. A mean satisfaction sparked in her. She'd wondered how long it would take Martin to resent the special attention Daniel had been paying her! Maybe he'd stay a bit closer to her from now on!

'So?' Derek was asking Daniel.

'The engine does seem good,' he nodded, placing his helmet on the roof of the car. He seemed totally unfazed by the exhibition of power driving he'd just been giving. Even his thick, dark hair was unruffled, his strong hands steady as granite. 'It's very noisy.'

'All the cars are going to be noisy this year, now that the regulations have changed,' Derek nodded. 'I'll be blunt, Daniel. I want you to drive this car. With Christian and Martin. And I need your answer now. Tomorrow will be too late.'

'Still the same Derek,' Daniel smiled. He turned laying a hand on Martin's shoulder. 'Well, *mon vieux*? Do you think I'm too old to take a last shot at Le Mans?'

'You're the best judge of that.' Martin's voice was cold. He shook his cousin's hand off his shoulder, and walked deliberately down the pits, every line of his body expressing resentment.

It was a childish piece of behaviour. Yet something inside Lili forgave him before it was even done. A feeling of culpability.

'What's up with him?' Derek chucked a thumb in Martin's direction.

'I don't think he particularly relishes sharing the car with me,' Daniel said, watching his cousin's back with concerned grey eyes. But Jacques Davel chuckled.

'*L'amour*. Love, that's what's wrong with him. You make him jealous, Daniel. You ought to know better by now.'

Daniel's eyes met hers, brooding and wise. She looked away, not wanting him to see too deeply into her own emotions.

'All right, Derek,' he said in his deep, husky voice. 'I'll drive.'

Amid the laughter and congratulations, Lili turned and followed Martin to soothe him.

'All my life I've been trying to do something on my

own,' Martin said bitterly. 'Trying to get out from under Daniel's shadow. But it seems he won't let me!'

'I'm sure he only wants what's best for you.' She stroked his hair, sorrow for him softening her eyes. They were alone together in the gymnasium at L'Hermitage, where Martin was supposed to be keeping fit in preparation for the race. 'He's very fond of you, my love.'

'Is he?' Martin was in a determined sulk. 'Sometimes I doubt it, babe. Sometimes I think he just likes to keep me round as a foil for himself.'

She shook her blonde head. 'What do you mean?'

'You know,' he said with a sour smile, 'like the court jester. That's why he wants me to join Maison Rouge. Useless cousin Martin, forced to hang around and show what a success Daniel Valais is!'

'That's not fair,' she said gently. A man like Daniel would hardly need a court jester to emphasise his manhood. She'd never seen Martin like this, had never realised how deep his resentment went, and it was a revelation.

'Nothing's fair,' he said. Clenching his teeth, he worked fiercely at the weights for a few seconds, then let them clatter back on to the rack. 'Everything I take up, everything that gives me a chance of succeeding in life, Daniel has to come along and take it away from me.' Lili said nothing. She'd always known that it was Martin's restlessness that had made him flit from one pursuit to another, but there just might be a glimmering of truth in what he was saying. 'Just like racing,' Martin was going on. 'As soon as I wanted to take it up, he tried to stop me. "You haven't the dedication, you will kill your young self."' It was a fair imitation of his cousin's husky voice, and Lili had to smile slightly.

'He's just concerned.'

'Yeah—concerned I'll actually achieve something.' He beat his knee with a clenched fist. 'I really wanted to do well at Le Mans, babe. It was a big thing for me—

like proving myself, if you like. Now Big Brother's going to be driving the car with me. And so, even if we win the race, people will say, "It was Daniel Valais's superb driving, as usual." Not Martin Petrov, but his big, successful, powerful cousin!'

'They won't,' Lili said persuasively. 'They're all expecting great things of you, Martin.'

'Well, I can't spend the whole day nattering,' he growled impatiently, and grasped the handles of the weight-lifting machine. 'You're in the way, if you don't mind.'

'Pardon me for breathing,' she said ironically, getting up to leave. To her relief, though, he'd started exercising again. The pre-race tension was obviously getting to him, finding out his weaknesses. She watched him for a few moments, remembering the day he'd stood watching her in this room. A shadow of doubt had been growing in her heart. She'd been so preoccupied by her own involvement with Daniel that she'd stopped thinking about the way Martin felt about *her*. Had there been an increasing indifference in his manner lately?

She shook the doubt away. She had to help him to stay calm in these tense few days, avoid upsetting him.

And that, she told herself firmly, meant being very cautious as far as Daniel was concerned. If Martin felt this way about his cousin, it would be cruel to give him any more cause for jealousy and insecurity.

CHAPTER SIX

LILI had gone to the small study overlooking the terrace, wanting to write some letters and just relax. But as she pushed the door open, Daniel was sitting at the window seat, talking on the telephone.

She apologised, and backed hastily out, but he looked up at her and covered the mouthpiece.

'Don't go,' he commanded quietly. 'I won't be a moment.'

Unwillingly, she came back in, and spread her papers out on one of the desks. Just being in the same room with Daniel was always enough to set her heart beating faster than normal. With half an ear, she was listening to his deep voice; her French was just good enough to tell her that he was delegating responsibility for the next few days.

He confirmed it a few minutes later when he put the receiver down. 'Someone has to run the show while I'm amusing myself,' he smiled. 'I'm getting a lot better at delegating than I was. I used to think I had to do everything personally. Now I enjoy my freedom more and more.' Supremely elegant in tailored grey slacks and a dark pullover, he rested his tall, lean figure against the window, and gestured towards the sophisticated stereo system. 'Why not put something nice on?'

She hunted through the vast collection of records beneath the system. Daniel's tastes ran to formal classical music. With a mind like his, she thought wryly, anything less than the best would be just noise.

'Brahms,' he said with a quirked eyebrow as she put one of her favourites on. 'I'd never have guessed.'

'Oh?' She let her eyes take in his deeply tanned face and thick black hair. 'Did you think my musical tastes ended with keep-fit pop medleys?'

'*Touché,*' he smiled. 'I should have remembered that Joan Lucas was an accomplished amateur pianist.'

'You've been checking up on me!' she challenged, her eyes widening in surprise.

'Well—I know some of the bare facts,' he nodded. 'What I don't know is the inner story. The stuff between the lines. Maybe you'll tell me one day.'

'There's practically nothing to tell,' she said with a little laugh at the subtle invitation. 'You're right, Joan was a fine pianist. She taught me to love music, but I'll never be as good a pianist as she was. I went to a good school, but I wasn't very academically inclined, either. When I left school, I worked in a record shop for a while, then a dress-shop in London. That's where I first started getting jobs modelling part-time.' She told him about the year she'd spent at the boutique, how the commissions had built up to a steady flow. 'It all might have come to nothing, except that *Charade* were looking for a fresh face for their next cover. I think they picked me because they happened to be running a spread on Juliet Maertens' designs, and I was one of the models. Someone liked my face.'

'I'm not surprised,' he said gravely. 'Hadn't you become a professional model by then?'

'You *have* been checking me out,' she accused, not sure whether to be shocked or flattered.

'I'm in the fashion business,' he reminded her, 'if only on the male side. It's not difficult to get rag-trade people to gossip. You could have gone on for a long time, though, keeping your safe, steady job at the shop, and modelling part-time. What prompted you to take the big gamble and leave?'

'I wasn't achieving,' she said simply. 'I was vegetating there, Daniel. You can't exactly fulfil yourself as a human being by watching overweight women try on twenty skirts in a row, or peeping to make sure the girl in booth three doesn't pinch anything!'

He laughed softly, deep-grey eyes dropping to study

her figure with disturbing appreciation. 'You must have had more than a dash of vanity, though, to set yourself up as a model.'

'That's what everyone thinks,' he said, her heart stirring at his scrutiny. 'But I just wanted to get out of my rut and see the world. I'd never thought of myself as beautiful or glamourous, or even moderately pretty.'

'Don't be silly,' he said, still smiling, 'you're one of the world's most beautiful women, *chérie*.'

'Don't tease me,' she said quietly.

'Tease you?' His eyes met hers. 'You seem to grow more beautiful every day, my love.'

I wish you wouldn't say things like that,' she said awkwardly, the memory of his touch all too clear in her heart.

'Like what?'

'About my being—beautiful.'

'You don't seem to understand,' he said quietly, moving forward to sit beside her, 'how much I care about you.'

'You can't care about another man's wife,' she said, nerves making her voice uneven.

'You're *not* another man's wife,' he snapped, eyes glittering. 'Wake up to reality, Lili.'

'I don't understand you,' she said shortly, her heart beating fast. 'You were the one who pushed Martin into setting a date for the wedding!'

'Yes—because I wanted to see the look in his eyes,' he growled. 'And you saw it, too. You don't think he means a word of that, do you?' She looked away, afraid he'd see the truth in her expression.

'Of course he means it,' she said woodenly. So that's why he'd done it—another little test.

'Listen to me, *ma petite*.' His voice was husky, urgent. 'It's time for us to talk plainly, because you're very innocent.' He grasped her left hand, holding it up before her face. 'What does that tell you, girl? He hasn't even bought you a ring!'

'There's a reason for that,' she said tensely, and told him.

'Oh, come on,' he said cynically when she'd finished. 'What kind of man would use that as an excuse?'

'Not everyone is wealthy and successful like you, Daniel,' she said, sounding a lot cooler than she felt. His onslaught had set her pulses racing, her mind spinning giddily. 'Some people have to wait for the things they want!'

'I know all about waiting for the things I want,' he said grimly. 'I've been doing it all my life. But rich or poor, the woman I was engaged to would have a ring to show the world that I meant what I said.'

'Martin means what he says, even if he hasn't been able to afford a ring,' she shot back. 'In fact, I admire him for wanting to wait until he can afford something better than the average. It's cruel of you to run him down when he's not here to defend himself.'

'He's never anywhere that you are,' Daniel pointed out acidly. 'He always seems to have something better to do than be with the woman he's supposed to be going to marry!'

'It's the run-up to Le Mans,' she said, wincing at the accuracy of that brutal statement. 'Unlike you, he has to work at it. And he's got things on his mind— including all the unfair pressure *you* keep putting on him.'

'Ah.' Irony carved deep lines either side of his sensuous mouth. 'He's been complaining about me to you, has he?'

'For heaven's sake,' she exploded, her clear voice rising in nervous exasperation, 'why do I always end up caught in the middle like this? Yes, he has been talking to me, Daniel. He's my fiancé. And I can't see that it's very wise of either of you to start a row just a few days before a major race, where you'll both be risking your lives!'

'That is true. But Martin worries me. I've seen him in this mood before, and it's dangerous. His concentration is going, *chérie*. The will to win just isn't there any more. I watch him going through the motions without any real drive, any real commitment. He's already lost interest in racing, but he won't admit it.'

'It's hardly surprising if his self-confidence is beginning to fade,' she shot back with a woman's indignation. 'You've done your best to smash it over the past weeks, haven't you!'

'You don't understand,' he said patiently, not responding to her accusation. 'It isn't me. It's a natural cycle in Martin's personality. Things interest him for just so long, and then, as soon as they begin to get difficult, his attention wanders. And I've told you before, a racing-driver whose attention wanders is a killer.'

He was trying to scare her. Or could it possibly be true? She would never question his judgment—if only she could be sure he wasn't playing some complex game of his own! 'I suppose you've been telling all this to Derek Brundle?' she said drily, thinking it would be just like his Machiavellian tactics to do so.

'No.' He shook his head emphatically. 'Derek is quite capable of making up his own mind about such things. As a sponsor, I never interfere, no matter who the driver is. Nor would I discuss a member of my family with an outsider, not ever Derek.'

'You're discussing him with me,' she reminded him pointedly.

'I regard you as a member of my family,' he said calmly. 'And that natural cycle I mentioned, Lili— you're being very naïve if you think it won't extend to you. He was fascinated with you because you were practically the only woman he'd ever met who didn't climb into his bed when he snapped his fingers. Oh, *chérie*,' he said drily, as she looked up at him sharply, 'I know you're a virgin. It's obvious in your beautiful face. Martin's not used to that—he's used to his good looks and charm getting him whatever he wants.'

'That's a despicable thing to say!' she accused hotly.

'If he is really serious about wanting to marry you, which I gravely doubt,' he went on grimly, 'all I can do is pray that his interest in you fades *before* you marry. And not *after*.' He took her face in his hands, fingers spreading to cup the lines of her cheekbones. 'Lili, I can see in your eyes that you think I'm a bad, selfish man.' She could only stare helplessly into the intensity of that deep-grey gaze. 'I'm not,' he said quietly. 'But I know Martin so much better than you do. I could tell you things about him——' He broke off, white teeth pinning his lower lip as if to bite back the words.

'Go on, then,' Lili snapped, anger uncurling inside her. 'Tell me all the terrible things you've been hiding, Daniel. I'm waiting to hear all about Martin—go on!'

His eyes were stormy clefts for a moment, and for a frightening second she thought he might really be about to reveal something awful about his cousin. Then he released her with a grimace.

'Forget I said that,' he grated.

'You don't *have* anything to tell me, do you?' she accused bitterly. 'Nothing except your blind prejudice against both of us, and your desire to get me into bed! What for? Just to take something else away from Martin?'

'I would watch my tongue if I were you,' he rasped ominously.

'I won't, Daniel! You've done your best to destroy what Martin and I had, and you've practically succeeded. Why can't you just leave us alone? I was so happy before I came to L'Hermitage. Now——' She broke off, almost in tears.

'If you're unhappy,' he said, more quietly, 'then there must be a deeper reason than my interference.'

'What are you getting at?' she choked.

'You *know* what I'm getting at. Your feelings for me—and mine for you. Have you forgotten what happened last Thursday?'

'*No!*' The memory of his magnificent body in her arms, his kiss transfiguring her, was shocking in the context of this argument. 'I can't deny that you're——' she hunted for a neutral word—'attractive. I'd be crazy to deny that. You've learned how to use your sexuality to dominate women—that's easy to see. But what happened then was an aberration, Daniel. And I'm not going to let you bend my will again, not ever!'

'What's your definition of an aberration?' he asked gently.

'Something abnormal,' she replied, her voice trembling and unsteady. 'Something that won't happen again.'

'Won't it?' His eyes dropped to study her slim woman's body, curled half-defensively in the leather chair. 'You're so sure. So desirable. So lovely.' He touched her face, making her shudder, tracing the tight curve of her flank, the caress ending on her thigh as he smiled slowly into her eyes. 'If you imagine that it won't ever happen again, my love, you're being very blind indeed.'

'It won't,' she said tightly. 'Not unless you choose to force me.'

'Force?' He mused over the word. 'No, Lili. That isn't what I want to do to you. I have no desire to conquer you. What I want is to see you admit your love for me. Not necessarily with words, *chérie*. Just a look in your eyes, a softness to that delectable mouth—that would tell me I have the right to carry you to my bed. To strip you naked. To make love to you with all my body and soul——'

'Stop!' she whispered, her hand covering that passionate male mouth to silence the words that were making her giddy. 'Don't say any more!'

He took her hand in both of his, kissing her palm, the fluttering pulse, the tips of her slim fingers. 'It's what we both want,' he said quietly, grey eyes meeting hers with an intimate understanding that made her weak.

'It's not what *I* want,' she denied in a whisper.

'I don't think you're even convincing yourself.' He kissed her with a tenderness that made her weak, his arms imprisoning her slender body against him. Suddenly she was as vulnerable as a trapped bird, her heart fluttering wildly, as though for release. But the gentle force of his embrace allowed no escape. His mouth was hungry, adoring, caressing her eyes, her temples, the soft skin of her yielding mouth, as though he could never possess enough of her.

'I mean to have you,' he told her, his deep voice vibrant with need. 'All of you, Lili. I want to kiss every inch of your skin, make love to you until the stars fall out of the sky.'

'Oh, Daniel,' she whispered brokenly, 'why must you do this to me?'

'Because you're mine. And because you're fooling yourself, *ma petite*.' He released her and rose, a dark, taut figure. 'As long as you keep fooling yourself, there's very little I can do. But you *are* fooling yourself, I promise you that. Maybe after Le Mans, when the carnival fades away, we'll all find out the truth about ourselves.'

She lay back in the chair, arms folded across her thudding, aching heart. After Le Mans? After Le Mans, she was getting as far away from Daniel Valais as she could.

She'd forgotten what peace of mind was like. This sense of being torn just couldn't continue, or she'd go crazy.

He was deliberately turning her against Martin. With hints and gestures and caresses and kisses, he was trying to warn her against the man she'd agreed to marry.

And such was his force of personality that she couldn't simply ignore him. He was so terribly attractive, able to sway her mind so easily. There was a kind of dark magic in him, a compulsion that made nonsense out of her self-control.

Inevitably, the doubts and uncertainties were growing. She hated herself for it, but it was true.

Like a pair of scales, unequally weighted, she was starting to tilt. Away from Martin, and towards the tall, dark man who obsessed her thoughts.

And he knew it. And took it as proof of her love for him.

The real question, if she could face it, was *why* he was able to dominate her emotions like this. Was it a purely sexual thing, some kind of potent chemistry that would fade once she was away from Daniel? Or was it something deeper and more complex?

If it was, then she felt she faced only one choice. To cancel her engagement with Martin, and to run, to the other side of the world, if necessary, from both of them.

But that was a last resort. Thank goodness for Barbados, and the clinical, unambiguous eye of the camera! She'd been away from work for long enough now; now it was time to pull herself together.

Before it was too late.

CHAPTER SEVEN

THE atmosphere at the track the next morning was of glittering excitement.

Daniel had hired one of the glassed-in lounges overlooking the pits, a rendezvous and hospitality area for Maison Rouge guests.

The plush, air-conditioned suite was crowded, even at the early hour they arrived. And overnight, the team seemed to have tripled in number. Lili found herself shaking hands with at least a dozen people she'd never seen before.

'Who *are* they all?' she asked Martin in a whisper, through the hubbub of greetings and laughter.

'Publicity people, extra mechanics, all sorts,' he shrugged. 'The bald man over there is Leslie Theobald, our technical boffin. He's in overall charge of the engines. Those two next to him are the chief chassis man and the gearbox wizard. You've met Jacques—he's the foreman mechanic. The rest are mechanics, tyre men, technical assistants, that kind of thing.' He smiled humourlessly. 'You're seeing Daniel in action.'

'And the girls?' she asked, looking at the half-dozen pretty young women who were ferrying champagne and canapés to and fro.

'Maison Rouge dolly-birds,' he grinned, looking his old self for a moment. 'Officially known as hospitality girls, and always easy on the eye. Sabrina Hobbs contracts them in to look after the VIPs—company directors, politicians, all the big-wigs who come here as guests of Maison Rouge.'

'I see,' she commented drily. They were all blonde, at least two of them natural, and they'd obviously been chosen to look sporty in bosom-and-bottom-hugging red cotton trouser-suits and Porsche caps. Women's liberation, she thought acidly, had yet to break into motor-racing. 'Very nice.'

'I think Lili disapproves of your dolly-birds,' Martin chuckled to Sabrina.

'Male guests love them,' was the answer, 'and so do the rest of the team. Lili, a couple of press people have requested interviews with you. If you want me to arrange a meeting, just say the word.'

'Interviews with *me*?' Lili queried in surprise.

'You're going to be in demand,' Sabrina smiled. 'Le Mans is probably the best-known, best-covered race in the circuit, and you add just the right touch of feminine glamour.' She outlined imaginary headlines with slim fingers. 'Beautiful model to wed young driving ace. Today's probably going to be too hectic, but I'll organise it for tomorrow, if you like. Excuse me.' She melted away in the direction of her hospitality girls, her expression indicating that one or more of them needed correction.

'Fame at last,' Lili smiled at Martin ruefully.

'I notice they don't want to interview *me*,' Martin grunted sourly.

Lili suddenly recognised a young Japanese woman, elegant in a white windcheater with white slacks making her way towards them through the crowd. She had two professional-quality cameras slung round her neck.

'Lili!' she beamed, 'I hoped you'd be here.'

'Iko, it's good to see you!' She worked with Iko Shikura in London on a few occasions at the beginning of last year, and had always been intrigued by Iko's strikingly beautiful, serene face. She remembered now having heard that Iko had moved to France about this time last year. 'What brings you to Le Mans?'

'My boss.' The Japanese girl laughed, showing pearly teeth. 'I'm working for Maison Rouge now.'

'No!'

'For the past six months,' Iko nodded happily. 'I

used to cover sports-car racing as well as fashion before I joined Maison Rouge, so Daniel sometimes asks me to cover big races like Le Mans for our publicity people. I don't have to ask why you're here,' she smiled, glancing at Martin. 'Hello, Martin. Congratulations to you both on your engagement.'

Martin, who was looking bored already, smiled a perfunctory greeting.

'I have to go somewhere,' he told Lili. 'Things to do.' He excused himself, and Lili was delighted with the chance to talk to Iko.

'I won't say it's dull being surrounded by so many handsome men,' she said to her friend, 'but I do miss female company. Tell me all your news.'

Iko had been doing well with Maison Rouge. She loved the work, she adored Daniel, and there was plenty of scope to be creative. 'Besides,' she added, waving at the surroundings, 'what other job would take me straight from a Berlin fashion-show to Le Mans?'

'You like motor-racing?'

'I love it,' Iko nodded. 'Almost as much as fashion. The only problem's the noise.'

'You're telling me,' Lili said ruefully. 'I don't know how I'm going to stand it.'

'Ah.' Iko unhooked a pair of plastic ear-defenders, like heavy-duty headphones, from round her neck, and gave them to Lili. 'Compliments of Maison Rouge. These'll help.'

'What's Daniel like to work for?' Lili couldn't help asking as she thanked Iko and put the ear-defenders in her bag.

'An inspiration,' Iko said simply. 'Everyone worships him. Some people are afraid of him, but I'm not. To me, he's the most intriguing man I've ever come across. You're staying at L'Hermitage, aren't you? I've been there once or twice to Daniel's parties. I don't call him Daniel to his face, by the way,' she asided with a grin.

'It's a fantastic place, isn't it?'

'Well, like Daniel himself, it's a little overpowering at first,' Lili smiled.

'I like my men overpowering,' Iko sighed, glancing across the room to where Daniel was deep in discussion with Leslie Theobald. Like Lili herself, Iko was in her early twenties and unmarried, and she'd once told Lili she liked it that way. She saw Iko's eyes drop to her bare ring-finger. 'When are you and Martin Petrov getting married?'

'Some time next year.'

'Planning a family?'

'I don't think either of us is very interested in children just yet,' she laughed.

'You're very lucky,' Iko told her. 'He's extremely handsome, like Daniel. But then, you're so beautiful. Why are you laughing?'

'Nothing. You're just rather direct,' Lili smiled.

'One of my un-Japanese failings. I'm sorry.' Iko offered Lili a cigarette, then lit one herself. 'It's also very un-Japanese for a woman to smoke,' she said apologetically, 'but I enjoy them.'

'I've never tried.' She took stock of Iko's flawless skin and raven hair. 'You know, I was expecting you to say that Daniel was rather a tartar to work for.'

'Never,' Iko shook her head emphatically. 'He's demanding, but I've never heard him blame anyone for an honest mistake. The only time I've ever seen him lose his cool was at Fuji, in Japan. That was the time your fiancé crashed, so it was to be expected.'

Lili slipped her hands into the pockets of her light cotton jacket. 'Was he really upset?'

'Well, you know that Martin's his closest relative. And there's a little rumour doing the company rounds that Daniel doesn't like the idea of *Martin le Malencontreux* racing——' She broke off, touching guilty fingers to her lips.

'Is that what they call him?' Lili asked quietly.

'"*Martin le Malencontreux*". That means "unlucky Martin". Why do they call him that?'

'It's just a joke,' Iko said quickly. 'He's so full of life, isn't he? A real original, always running at full throttle. It's just that now and then—well, he did have that accident at Fuji.' She looked uncomfortable. 'French humour, Lili, that's all.' It sounded insincere, and as though recognising that, Iko changed the subject. 'Isn't it wonderful that Daniel's going to drive? It gives you a real kick to work for someone like that. Maison Rouge is a gigantic company, you know, and yet he makes it feel like a family. There's something about him that seems to touch everyone he employs. You know how the French are about Le Mans . . .' She glanced at the watch on her slim brown wrist. 'I have to be down at the pits right now—they're going to be testing the car, and I want some shots.'

'I'll see you down there,' Lili smiled, and Iko disappeared through the crowd with a wave.

She made her way to a secluded niche by the window, and stared down, still thinking about that nickname. Maybe Martin was right, maybe he *was* doomed to go through life being unfairly compared to his cousin. Even if he excelled at motor-racing, there would probably still be someone to point out that Daniel had done better, to call him Martin the unlucky.

The tarmac was starting to shimmer in the heat, and there were more cars on the track. Below her, the pit lane was crowded with technicians, photographers, drivers, managers. She was getting used to the scream of the engines as the cars hurtled up the straight, the howls of protest as the drivers changed down for the first bend.

Such a frantic world. So much money. Daniel had told her that each car was worth hundreds of thousands; a set of wheels alone might cost the price of a new Cadillac, and there were piles upon piles of them in the workshop areas.

The level of sponsorship was staggering, even though she was used to the extravagant world of international fashion. Every inch of the bodyshell—and even some of the drivers' overalls—seemed to be utilised, advertising motor-oil, shock-absorbers, cigarettes, banking, anything you cared to mention.

Daniel, through the company, must be pouring a fortune into the endurance championship.

But with an experienced model's understanding of publicity, Lili had worked out that the rewards were equally vast. Television coverage meant that the Maison Rouge name would be appearing on fifty million screens across the world. An outright win would be an incalculable advertising coup.

And in the meantime, the glamour of motor-racing would be rubbing off on the company's name. It would obviously make a considerable impact on potential customers when Daniel could invite their directors and top buyers to the special suite at Le Mans, the special trailer at Monza.

'So this where you've been hiding, *chérie*.' She felt Daniel's arms slide around her waist, pulling her back against his hard, virile body. 'You look like a lost little girl,' he whispered huskily in her ear. 'I can't resist you.'

'Pepple will see!' she protested, but the outrage just wasn't there. Instead of struggling, she was nestling back ecstatically into the exciting comfort of his embrace. When he touched her, she felt so secure, so warmed inside.

'Are you bored?' he murmured, voice warm against her skin.

'No,' she whispered. She arched her neck back, knowing the silky, scented swathe of her hair would caress his mouth. She hugged his iron-hard arms around her, feeling herself melting inside, all over again. 'Please,' she begged unsteadily, 'let me go. Everyone will wonder!'

'Why should they? I'm going to be your relation

soon.' He turned her to face him, pulling her
shamelessly close, so that their bodies were pressed hard
together. 'Why do you always smell so bewitching?' he
growled, eyes intoxicatingly intent on her face. 'I half-
believe you brew your own potions just to torment me!'

'I don't.' The thrust of his hips was bone-meltingly
sexual against her, deliberately erotic. He *knew* what he
did to her, and loved it! 'Daniel, please! Someone will
come.'

'Let them.' He kissed her lips, hungrily. 'Do we really
care?' He was looking brutally male in a black flame-
proof suit with the Porsche and Maison Rouge logos
embroidered over the breast. 'Any ideas where Martin
is?'

'He was here a moment ago.' She almost whimpered
as he let her go. For all her protesting, she only felt
half-alive when he wasn't near her, and it was a sharp
pang to be released from that so-potent embrace. She
rose on tiptoe to peer over heads. 'He said he had
something to do.'

'He's meant to be taking the car out,' Daniel said
with a flicker of irritation. 'I'll try the garage.' He
smiled into her eyes, making her weak at the knees.
'Don't run away. I'll be back.'

But by one o'clock, Martin still hadn't turned up.

He'd missed his drive. Derek Brundle was impatient
and angry, having despatched half a dozen people to
find him, and Daniel was grim-faced. Lili had looked
everywhere for him, but the paddock was jammed with
spectators and officials, and it was like looking for a
needle in a very, very big haystack.

Lunch was served by Sabrina Hobb's minions in the
sunlit service area between the bigger of the two trailers
and the mechanic's marquee.

Lili found herself sitting under a giant sun-umbrella
with Daniel and three or four others.

Daniel was uncommunicative, his tanned face

expressionless as he ate. Lili left her Dior sunglasses on, not feeling much like conversation either. It was hot, and the distant snarling of engines persisted as she picked without much appetite at a delicious cold chicken salad. Absently, she listened to a very technical discussion beside her between Jacques Davel and Christian Seberg about the latest fuel regulations.

Martin, she thought tiredly, could sometimes be infuriating. Maybe this morning's absence was designed as an elaborate kind of gesture. Maybe he was simply sulking. There was no way of telling. What was certain was that disappearances like this were exactly calculated to convince Daniel that he was still irresponsible, that he couldn't be relied upon. And it wasn't going to impress Derek Brundle, either. It just weakened his own position. What *made* him behave like this?

Just then, a little ripple of laughter made her look up. Martin was making his way over to their table, looking as though he hadn't a care in the world. She didn't know whether to be more relieved or apprehensive as he sat down, grinning broadly, and helped himself to the bowls of salad.

'I've been into town,' he announced to the table at large. 'Sorry I missed my drive. I'll take the car this afternoon.'

'Indeed.' Christian was smiling tolerantly, but Daniel's eyes were Baltic grey as he looked up at Martin. 'May we ask what you were doing in town all morning?'

'Shopping.' He pushed a forkful of chicken into his mouth, then fished a little leather box out of his pocket. He tossed it casually across the table to Lili. 'Something for you.'

Why in heaven's name didn't he have the brains to apologise, at least look contrite? She picked up the little box, and opened it.

Inside was a diamond ring.

Feeling her heart miss a beat, she lifted it

disbelievingly out of the velvet padding. A big stone, dazzlingly bright in the sunlight, set in an ornate golden setting. In the silence that had fallen, Christian Seberg let out a long whistle of admiration.

'Oh, *là là*.' Jacques leaned across the table to stare at the ring with wide eyes. 'Now that's a ring worthy of Lili Bergman! Where did you get that chunk of ice, *mon vieux*?'

'It's an antique.' Martin was obviously revelling in the minor sensation he'd caused. 'Eighteenth century, so the jeweller says. Belonged to a Comtesse.'

Lili was still gaping, her emotions a mixture of disbelief and something almost like fear. As if sharing her feelings, Daniel asked quietly, 'Where did you get it?'

'An antique jeweller's,' Martin smiled, 'in *le vieux Mans*.'

'The old quarter,' Jacques said. 'That's the place to find treasures. It looks absolutely priceless. Well, go on,' he grinned at Lili, 'put it on!'

'It might be a little large,' Martin said, tucking into his chicken with relish. 'Any jeweller can reduce it if it is.'

Lili slid the ring over her third finger, an odd sensation accompanying the gesture. The ring was undeniably exquisite, and yet there was a dull, cold feeling in her heart. The expression on Daniel's face was watchful. He reached for Lili's hand, his fingers warm around her own, and studied the ring.

'It's absolutely beautiful,' Lili said with a catch in her voice. 'How could you possibly afford it?'

'I've blown my entire savings,' Martin said calmly. 'Everything, every *franc*.'

'Oh, Martin,' she said gently.

'*C'est l'amour, quoi d'autre*?' Jacques Davel chuckled. 'The boy takes after you, Daniel!'

'He wanted far more than I had,' Martin said, looking at the ring reminiscently. 'I fell in love with it the moment I saw it. I knew I had to buy it for Lili. But all I had was the money I'd taken out of my account, which was almost fifteen thousand francs less than he wanted. So I said, "Look, monsieur, I must have the ring for my fiancée, and this is all I have," and I put the money on the counter in front of him.'

'What did he say?' Christian asked, obviously fascinated.

'Well, he hummed and hawed a bit, but in the end he said, "Go on, take the thing before I change my mind!" So I shot out, clutching my treasure. I haven't been as pleased for years.' He grinned at Lili's stunned expression. 'You didn't think I had it in me, did you? Anyway, I hope you like it.'

'I love it,' she said, trying to sound as delighted as she knew she should be.

'Trust Martin to just chuck it across the table like that,' Christian laughed. Derek Brundle had come over to see what the commotion was about; by the expression on his face, Martin was in for a blasting, until Derek saw the ring on Lili's finger.

'So that's what you've been doing all morning,' he guessed, his frown easing despite himself. 'Your timing's rotten, Martin, but that looks a nice rock.'

Sabrina Hobbs, too, was ooh-ing over the ring, and the hospitality girls had crowded round. Lili felt faintly absurd, extending her slim fingers for everyone to admire the glittering ring Martin had so coolly dropped in her lap.

Only Daniel was still stony-faced, his grey eyes flicking from her to Martin.

'There you are, Daniel,' Martin said smugly, turning to his cousin at last with the air of someone who's played an ace. 'You wanted me to buy her a ring—what do you think of that?'

'I think you'd better finish your lunch and get into your suit,' Daniel said grimly. 'Jacques needs to work on the car this afternoon, so you don't have much time.'

'My boys and I can work late,' Jacques said, obviously feeling sorry for Martin. 'Go easy on the lad, Daniel! It's not every day a man buys a diamond for his wife-to-be.'

'It's not every day a man competes at Le Mans, either,' Derek said shortly. 'Daniel's right. You'd better get your drive in as soon as possible, Martin.'

'Aye, aye.' Martin gave them a mock-naval salute, and stuffing a last fork-load in, pushed his chair away from the table. He marched off in the direction of the trailer, singing, 'Hi ho, hi ho, it's off to work we go,' through a mouthful of chicken salad. Lili heard Sabrina giggling behind her. But the situation was far from funny.

This kind of wildly unpredictable behaviour was disturbing, not amusing. And that escape-hatch she'd thought of yesterday—dissolving her engagement and running away from both of them—had just been slammed shut. She couldn't very well throw back the ring he'd spent his last penny on. She glanced covertly at Daniel, who was finishing his meal in total silence. Had he been equally disturbed by this morning's events?

As if feeling her eyes on him, he looked up, his dark gaze making her heart jump. 'Do you want to watch Martin practising?'

'I think—think I should,' she replied. She touched the stop-watch round her neck. 'Some of the crew were showing me how to time the laps this morning——'

'We've got three computers to do our lap-timing for us,' he pointed out gently. 'I'll drive you out to the Mulsanne straight. You'll get a much better view from there.'

'Oui,' Jacques agreed, 'the Mulsanne is the heart of Le Mans.'

'Thanks, then,' she said, smiling a little tightly. She knew it was tempting fate to be alone with Daniel, yet there was something which drew her to him like a dragnet, against her will. She stared down at the brilliant diamond on her third finger. Martin hadn't even given her a kiss with it, she thought absently. There had been so little ceremony about it. Yet it must have cost him every penny he had—and then some— and she ought to be deeply grateful.

Was it a token of sincere love? Or just an extravagant gesture? Cursing herself for the cynical thought, she rose to follow Daniel's tall figure.

He drove the Ferrari carefully through the throngs of people along the concourse, under the tunnel, and out of the main gates. It was a hot, sunny day, and Lili was glad of the air-conditioning in the leather-trimmed cockpit of the car.

'I'll take you to *Les Hunaudières*,' he said, accelerating through a gap in the traffic. 'That's where all the filmstars gather. And the coffee there is better than Sabrina Hobbs's, at any rate.'

'She does a marvellous job,' Lili said. 'In fact, the organisation is staggering all round.' She glanced at his profile. 'I guess you've all done this a lot of times before.'

'A lot of times,' he smiled.

'How do you feel about driving?' she ventured. 'I mean, you said you were getting too old—though that's crazy,' she added hastily as his brows lifted in amused irony. 'I mean, you look superb.' She cursed her blundering tongue. 'Is the car going well?'

'I don't think I'm out of my depth, if that's what you mean,' he said. 'I'm not quite a geriatric yet, Lili. I'm only thirty-four.'

'That's a perfect age for a man,' she said in a small voice.

'Twelve years older than you,' he pointed out, shooting her a glance from under thick, dark lashes. 'Do you feel that puts me in a different generation?'

'No. It just——' She struggled to find the words. 'Sometimes you make me feel like a child, that's all. And I know you do it to Martin, too.'

'But neither of you are children,' he said quietly. His hands were sure on the wheel, strong fingers curled relaxedly round the leather-clad rim. She looked at her ring again, studying the ornate, antique setting with troubled eyes.

The terrace of the famous bar called *Les Hunaudières* overlooked the three-mile-long Mulsanne straight, the longest, fastest stretch in all motor-racing. It was crowded, but they found a table with a good view, and Daniel ordered coffee while Lili watched the track in awe. The cars were moving at a terrifying pace, their engines snarling at the very peak of their performance. Like brilliantly-coloured rockets, they hurtled past at speeds well over two hundred miles an hour.

'God, it's terrifying,' she said. From the grandstands, the cars were just noisy blurs of colour that were gone in a flash. With this view along the tree-lined straight, you could see just how frighteningly fast they were going, could see them weaving as the faster cars went through the groups of slower ones.

'There's Martin,' he pointed out. She watched the red and gold car in silence. It howled past them, and on towards the distant bend, giving her a fleeting glimpse of a helmeted head through the curved windshield. For the first time, she was beginning to understand just how dangerous a sport this was. On television it had looked so safe and easy. But out here, the naked, appalling danger was only inches away.

She looked up at Daniel. 'When I said you made Martin feel like a child,' she said, 'I meant that in a good sense as well as a bad one. He looks up to you a lot more than he'll admit, Daniel.'

'Yes.' He was staring with brooding eyes at a TV company helicopter hovering high above the track. 'We used to be far closer than we are now. Since he left school, we've been growing apart more and more.'

'He's a very different person from you,' she said,

stirring her coffee. 'That's odd, considering how closely you're related.'

'Our parents were very different people.'

'I've never met Martin's father.' She hesitated. 'Tell me about him—and your mother.'

'Well,' he smiled slightly, 'what do you know?'

'Their names were Ivan and Claudia Petrov,' Lili supplied. Martin had told her that much. 'And they were Romanian aristocrats who moved to Switzerland.'

'Yes,' he nodded. 'Martin's father came to the west with my mother——' He calculated rapidly in his mind. '—almost exactly thirty-seven years ago. The young Baron of Rodna-Vecha and his sister, the last of their line.' He looked up as the chopper drifted slowly overhead, the cameras on board following the cars as they breasted the tree-lined hill before the curve. 'Of course,' he went on, 'even then the title was meaningless. If it were not,' he smiled slightly, 'it would be Martin who would inherit the baronetcy, not I.'

'Funny,' she said thoughtfully, 'you're so much more the nobleman than he is.' The statement was gauche, all too revealing, but he didn't seem to notice. 'How old were they?'

'A little younger than you are now. My mother was eighteen, Martin's father twenty-one. When our grandfather died, they took what remained of the family fortune—some icons, a few jewels, some rare manuscripts—and drove the Bugatti to Switzerland.' Grey eyes were on hers again, with surprising gentleness. 'Has Martin told you about my parents?'

'Only that they died when you were a boy,' she answered, studying his profile.

'My mother is dead,' he confirmed. 'As for my father, I have no idea whether he is alive or not.'

'You haven't?' she asked, green eyes wide.

'I never knew him, Lili. I was born in Geneva, a year or so after Claudia and Ivan arrived. My father was a very senior official in one of the embassies, but the resultant scandal was very effectively hushed up. You can imagine how the tongues wagged—the devastatingly beautiful young refugee, the distinguished diplomat. My mother never disclosed my father's name, not even to me. All she would say was that he was a good, kind man who loved her dearly. He only had one grave fault.'

'What was that?' she asked, so fascinated she'd forgotten the cars hurtling past them a few hundred yards away.

'He happened to be married to someone else.' He touched her cheek with a strange half-smile. 'He wanted to acknowledge me, but neither my mother nor his government would let him. There were political complications, you see.'

'Martin's never mentioned this!' she said in astonishment.

'Martin is rather ashamed of my bastard origin. He doesn't like to have it mentioned.' His eyes challenged her. 'Does it disturb you?'

'Of course not! But it's such a strange, haunting story. Why isn't your name Petrov, then, like Martin's?'

He laughed gently. 'It is, I suppose. But after I was born, my mother went to live in small villa near Zermatt, called Maison Rouge. I named my company after that house,' he nodded, in response to her enquiring look. 'She was very happy there. That was where I grew up, under the shadow of the Alps.'

'How does that explain your name?'

'Zermatt is in the canton of Valais,' he smiled. 'She liked the name, I think, so she took it as her own.'

'So that's it,' she said thoughtfully. 'Did you never want to change your own name back?'

'I thought about it,' he nodded. 'But I decided against it. I had no title to my father's name, even if I knew it. And since my mother had wanted to leave the name of Petrov behind her, I eventually decided to do the same.' He shrugged slightly. 'It was a new start, a new life, a new age, even. I preferred to let the name of Petrov die out—in my branch of the family, at any rate.'

She looked down at her hands, the ring sparkling on her slender finger. Her children, if she had any, would be called Petrov. If she married Martin. *When* she married Martin. Again it occurred to her that she almost never thought about her married life with Martin, or the family they might have together. It was time she started planning things more seriously.

'What was your mother like?' she asked.

He glanced at her. 'You mean in appearance? She was very beautiful. Black eyes, black hair, skin as white as milk. Very aristocratic, very passionate, a true Romanian.'

'Your father must have had blue eyes, then,' she mused aloud, 'because yours are slate-grey.' She looked up guiltily at his chuckle. 'Oh, I'm sorry. I shouldn't speculate about such a delicate topic—forgive me! Tell me more about your mother.'

'I was only a child when she died,' he reminded her. 'Like all children, I suppose, I thought she was wonderful. Whenever I see her in my mind's eye, Lili, she is always singing or laughing.' He leaned forward, resting his chin on a hard-looking fist. 'Why are you asking all these questions?'

'Just catching up,' she said shyly. The truth was that he fascinated her utterly. 'Martin hardly ever talks about his family, so it's nice to get all the details from an unimpeachable source! Why do you say your mother was so different from Martin's father?'

'She was completely unconcerned about conventions, a woman of great personality. But she was always deeply honest, almost painfully so at times, in fact.'

That was a trait he appeared to have inherited, Lili thought wryly, but didn't say the words out loud.

'And Ivan?'

'Ivan was a wastrel, self-indulgent without my

mother's honesty. A handsome young man who slid gradually into decadence.' Daniel's face was sad. 'He lived for a few years on the money he made selling off his share of the family treasure, and by sponging on friends in Geneva. Then he had a stroke of luck. He entranced a pretty little Englishwoman called Lucy Arbuthnot, who was holidaying in Switzerland. The Arbuthnots were a rich shop-keeping family. Somehow he convinced them all that he had millions stashed away in some secret bank-account in Geneva.' A brief, wolfish smile crossed his face. 'They were delighted to have snared such a glamorous and wealthy young aristocrat for their daughter. Ivan and Lucy settled in Geneva, in an apartment conveniently close to all Ivan's drinking-haunts. Martin was born a year later. The same year that you were born.'

Lili digested this in an uncomfortable silence. Martin had never told her any of his family history, and she wondered whether he could ever have been as brutally frank as Daniel. 'I take it the marriage didn't last,' she said sadly.

'No. It was already showing signs of strain when Martin was born. Ivan liked wine, women other than his wife, and song. Much too much. Having wasted the last of the patrimony he and Claudia brought with them, he started making large inroads into the Arbuthnot fortune via Lucy's inheritance. The respectable Arbuthnots were beginning to wonder whether the marriage had been such a good idea, after all.' White teeth glinted in an ironic chuckle. 'In August of that same year, my mother had an accident in the Bugatti. She was killed immediately. I had just had my eleventh birthday.'

Lili couldn't help shivering, gooseflesh appearing on her fine skin. 'What happened to you?'

'My mother's nationality was still unresolved at the time of her death.' He drained his cup, eyes sombre. 'They put me under the care of the *Haut Commissariat*

pour les Réfugiés. That's the UN organisation which
had been helping my mother. They arranged for me to
live in a succession of foster-homes until I was
eighteen.'

'You must have hated that,' she said quietly, thinking
of the blissful life he must have enjoyed in the villa
called Maison Rouge.

'There was no one else to take me.' He laid a warm
hand on hers, sending an intimate shock through her
system. 'You were lucky, at least, in that you had Joan
Lucas.'

She hesitated, then stroked his hand with sensitive
fingertips. 'Yes,' she nodded. 'My life would have been
very different but for Joan.' Involuntarily, her fingers
were lacing through his, clasping his big, tanned hand
between both her own. 'I wish there had been someone
there for you. How long were you in foster-homes?'

'Five or six years, until I finished my schooling. Then
I started work at a clothing factory in Geneva.' They
fell silent as a group of seven or eight cars flew along
the straight, the deep noise of the engines filling the air.
The afternoon sky spread over them, magnificent as a
Constable landscape. 'By that time Martin's parents
were divorced and living separate lives. Lucy had more
or less given up on them both, and had gone back to
England.' He grimaced. 'She had a nervous breakdown
that was almost certainly a result, at least in some part,
of the miserable life Ivan had led her all those years.
Ivan himself was degenerating into alcoholism, though
he was only forty.'

'Alcoholism?' she questioned. 'But Ivan remarried,
didn't he, and lives in Switzerland now!'

'Is that what Martin told you?' Daniel's eyes
softened. 'Ivan's in Switzerland, yes—but in a clinic for
advanced alcoholics.'

'Oh, no,' she whispered, feeling a deep pang of pity
for Martin. So he had lied to her . . . She thought back
to the gaily-painted face, the vacant eyes, of Lucy

Petrov. She couldn't blame Martin for drawing a veil over the truth. His parents' lives were a tragedy that must haunt him.

'And you? What happened to you?'

'Always me,' he smiled. 'So, increasingly, I had to take on the care of both my unfortunate uncle Ivan and my cousin Martin, who was then, I suppose, rising five or six.'

'How could you possibly look after them?' Lili asked in awe. 'You could only have been eighteen yourself!'

'I had no choice,' he said calmly. 'They were my only relations, Lili, and I'd become the man of the family. I didn't want Martin to end up in a foster-home, the way I did.' His fingers closed round her hand, possessive, comforting. 'However, it was obvious that Ivan needed help. I arranged for psychiatrists, alcoholics' associations, even priests, to assist him. None of them ever did any good, and in the end he had to go into an institution. I eventually got him into a place at San Giovanni, a beautiful monastery near the Great St Bernard. He's more or less happy there. I visit him now and then, but Martin never does. He can't bear it, and anyway, Ivan doesn't know anybody.'

'It's so sad,' Lili said, feeling the lump in her throat. 'Was Martin badly affected as a boy?'

'He knew very little about it,' Daniel sighed. When he was twelve, I sent him to school in England. I wanted him to be a gentleman, you see, bring credit on the family name—as well as get him away from Ivan.' He made a slightly bitter face. 'I should have faced up to my responsibilities and brought the boy up myself. I should have anticipated that with a father like Ivan, and a mother as weak as Lucy, he would grow up to be unruly and wilful. But I have to admit I was also too busy with Maison Rouge. That is the one great regret I have.'

'You make him out worse than he is,' she smiled tentatively. Her emotions were so mixed—one part of her loved him for his care of Martin, another part was afraid of his sternness. 'He doesn't exactly do you discredit, Daniel.'

'I am glad you are so loyal to him,' he said, unsmiling. 'Perhaps I am too harsh—I know him better, you see. I expect more from him.'

'Tell me more about those early days,' she invited, avoiding the dangerous topic.

'In the meantime I was learning a lot at that factory. About making things work, the way business operated, the way people made money. After two years I started putting those lessons into practice. I named my factory Maison Rouge, after the house in Zermatt where my mother had lived.' He smiled briefly. 'Actually, the villa was pink, rather than red, but the name had impact. What the ad-men call "resonances".'

'Was Maison Rouge an immediate success?'

'More or less,' he nodded. 'My idea was very simple—stylish, elegant clothes for men, at reasonable prices. I hired the half-dozen best young designers who'd graduated that year, and gave them a completely free hand.' His eyes glinted at hers, amethyst-grey under black lashes. 'You're too young to remember, but at that time, clothes for men were incredibly drab. Even the so-called "young" fashions for rebellious youngsters were just variations on what their fathers were wearing. When my clothes went on sale, full of colour and style, the entire men's clothing industry thought I'd gone mad.' He smiled. 'I was a millionaire, though—on paper, at least—when I was twenty-four. Around the time that you were starting high school.' He broke off, the smile disappearing.

'What is it?' she asked in alarm at his tight expression.

'A crash.' She followed his pointing finger to where a pall of smoke was drifting into the air a mile or two away.

'Oh, no,' she whispered in sudden panic.

'It's not Martin,' he said shortly. 'I've just seen him go by.' The public address system had crackled into a torrent of French, and Daniel listened intently. 'One of the Renaults,' he translated. 'The driver is slightly hurt, but he's safe.'

'Thank God!'

'I hate to see that sight.' He stared with arctic eyes at the smudge of black against the blue sky. 'Every year there's someone. Every few years, a death.' He took her left hand, looking into her eyes. 'I want to ask you something, Lili.'

'What?' she smiled.

'This ring.' Involuntarily, she glanced down at the glittering diamond. 'Don't wear it.'

'Don't wear it?' she echoed, taken aback. 'Why on earth not?'

'If I asked you not to wear it for my sake,' he said softly, 'would you?'

'No!' she said angrily. Was this why he'd brought her out here? 'It's my engagement ring, the one you bullied the poor boy into buying! And he's spent every penny he had on it. Of course I'm going to wear it!'

'It will bring you bad luck,' he said, his voice roughening as his eyes darkened to anthracite-grey.

'What's that,' she demanded, 'some sort of premonition?' She was offended and annoyed by the extraordinary request, even though what he'd told her about his family had given her a new insight into his compassion and generosity. 'I'm going to wear it, Daniel!'

'Very well.' His mouth grim, he rose abruptly. In his anger he was an intimidating figure. There was no mistaking his masculine power; it was evident in the hard promise of his body, the play of muscle under the superbly elegant clothes. Martin was handsome, one of the handsomest men she'd seen; but Daniel had an impact, an authority that vibrated with leashed strength. She knew exactly why Martin was in so much awe of him.

'Wear it if you must. We'd better get back,' he said, the mood of intimacy now definitely over. 'There are things to do.'

CHAPTER EIGHT

LESS than forty-eight hours to the start of the race, and the tempo of life seemed to have accelerated. Le Mans was the sole topic on television and in the papers. Three reporters had asked for brief interviews with Lili, and at least one story had appeared in the Le Mans press, complete with a picture of her and an unsmiling Martin.

The photograph reflected the reality. Since giving her the ring, Martin had hardly spoken two words to Lili. It wasn't just that she saw little of him; when he was with her, he was silent and obviously nervous. She had to simply accept that he would show signs of strain before every race, at least every big race like Le Mans.

Thursday afternoon was a free period. The cars were with the mechanics, and the general public had started invading the paddock and the camping-sites in earnest now. By Saturday afternoon, some quarter of a million people or more would have assembled to watch the start.

Martin was resting in his room, having made it clear he didn't want company, and Daniel had taken the Range Rover down to the apple orchards, in the company of his farm manager. At a loose end for once, she decided to take a swim in the pool.

The indoor pool was one of the most beautiful features of L'Hermitage. It was set in what had once been the conservatory, adjoining the library. The great high-ceilinged hall with its domed glass roof and gigantic arched windows between tall marble columns had been an inspired site for a pool. The water-temperature always seemed to be perfect, and the expanses of glowing white marble and white-framed glass gave it a timeless, cool beauty.

Lili paused for a moment on the diving-board, tying back her golden hair, a slim figure in her black one-piece. The sky was almost cloudless above the high glass dome, the sun streaming down into the clear depths below.

Then she dived cleanly into the water, and broke into an easy crawl. She'd always loved swimming, and she let her mind drift into neutral as she cruised up and down the deep-blue pool, feeling her body moving with relaxed, smooth co-ordination.

After twenty laps she stopped, and pulled herself out of the water, panting. She shook her hair back in a dripping, golden arc, and padded wetly across the tiles to where she'd left her towel.

Abruptly, her heart jolted inside her. Daniel was leaning against the marble column by her towel, watching her with intent grey eyes.

'Oh—I didn't see you there!' She shook water from her hands, her long hair clinging inelegantly around her face. 'How long have you been there?' she asked, still slightly out of breath.

'A few minutes.' Black made his formidable good looks even more dramatic, intimidating, even, the wide leather belt emphasising the narrowness of his waist, the power of his shoulders.

'I hope you don't mind me using the pool—I just felt I needed to keep in shape.'

'You look in perfect shape to me,' he said softly. She was acutely aware of his eyes on her, following the rise and fall of her breasts, dropping to caress the shape of her body under the gleaming wet swimsuit. It was clinging to her tightly, and she knew it must leave very little to his imagination.

'It's—it's a beautiful pool, Daniel.' His gaze was too intense to bear; she picked up the fluffy white towel, and pressed it to her face, hiding behind its welcoming modesty. He moved to her with the leisurely fluidity of a leopard, gently pulling the towel out of her hands,

dropping it at her naked feet. 'Don't hide yourself from
me,' he commanded in a quiet growl. 'Unless you want
to tantalise me, Lili. Do you?'

'I—no, I don't,' she stammered, trying to smile. It
was both frightening and exciting to sense how aroused
he was at the sight of her near-naked body. The
moment was dangerous. She was acutely conscious of
her long, naked legs, the thinness of the material that
clung to her like a second skin. 'I—I think I'd better
take a shower——'

'Stay.' His fingers were like velvet-gloved steel around
her wrists, imprisoning her. 'Let me look at you.'

'I'm just a woman,' she said in a low voice, 'like a
billion others.' She could hardly bear to look into his
eyes. She knew that the passion she would see in them
would destroy what little composure she was still
clinging to.

'Not like a billion others. Unique. You move like a
dancer, Lili. Smooth and sensuous and utterly,
completely desirable.'

'I've begged you not to talk like that,' she said in an
uneven whisper. She dropped her head, her mouth
quivering with tension. 'It's cruel . . .'

'It's not meant to be cruel, my beautiful one.' He
took her chin in his hand, turning her face upwards so
that he could look down into it with compelling, hungry
eyes. 'You and I aren't separate people, my love. We're
the same person, except that we haven't come together
yet. And I find it a great strain trying to hide my
feelings for you—especially at a moment like this.'

'And what are they?' she asked painfully. 'Lust,
desire?'

His smile was a mixture of mockery and tenderness.
'That comes into it, *chérie*. But there is more, a great
deal more. My heart and my soul, for a start.' She
closed her eyes helplessly as he bent to her. She felt his
first, clinging kiss, his tongue tracing the perfect leaf-
shape of her lips with slow, devastating thoroughness.

She whispered his name, her lips parting helplessly against his. His arms closed around her, possessing her, pressing her wet body against his.

'Let's stop here,' she pleaded, her pulses pounding in her ears. 'It's crazy to do this.'

Daniel laughed huskily, the desire in his eyes bold as sin. 'What's crazy is trying to deny it, Lili. Some day the dam walls just have to burst.'

'I love Martin,' she moaned.

'You can't.' She flinched as he stroked the wet tumble of her hair. 'You can't love Martin, my sweet one. Because you already love someone else.'

The words were like a sword driven deep into her heart. 'That's not true!'

He cupped the delicate oval of her face in his hands, eyes brooding on her mouth. 'You think not? I've been holding myself in ever since the day you came to my house, Lili. Shall I prove that it *is* true?'

Her fingers closed round his wrists shakily. 'I—I think I'd better go, Daniel. Before——'

'Before you acknowledge your own feelings?' He kissed her eyes, his lips tasting the tears that had begun to gather on her long lashes.

'Even if what you think were true,' she whispered, 'I could never do it to Martin. He needs me!' She was as helpless as a sail in a hurricane, filled and dominated by Daniel's kisses. She could only cling to his broad shoulders, her lips parting under the thrust of his tongue.

Only Daniel could fill her senses like this, make her respond in this infinitely sensual way. He was the most masculine man she'd ever met. His maleness was overwhelming, a quality that had dominated her reactions to him from the start. It was as though he'd left some secret chemical in her blood, a recurrent fever thst would always explode into flame at his touch.

'My darling,' he said huskily against her wet throat. 'My little virgin. What if I were to make love to you,

here, now? Would Martin still be so eager to have you
as his bride?' He slid his fingers under the shoulder-
straps of her swimsuit, slipping them over her
shoulders, drawing them down gently until the wet
material peeled away from the curving swell of her
breasts, leaving them naked to his warm lips.

As though caught in some dark spell, Lili could only
cling to him with pounding heart, her lashes closing
over dimming green eyes. She felt his lips touch each
tender peak of her breasts in an almost reverent kiss.
Martin had touched her breasts, too, but never with the
same controlled passion, and never shaking her with the
almost frightening pleasure she felt now.

'My love,' he whispered huskily, 'not even the water
can wash the scent from your skin. You always smell so
sweet, it haunts me, drives me crazy . . .'

Her legs could no longer support her. He lowered her
to the smooth marble at the water's edge, kneeling to
claim the satin-soft mouth she offered him. The kissing
gave way to another kind of hunger, a driving need
inside her that urged her against him, forcing a
whimper from her throat as his hand cupped her breast.
He brushed his thumb lingeringly across the aroused
peak, teasing it into a concentrated star of yearning.

'You're shaking like a leaf,' he said wonderingly,
cradling her in his arms. It was true; she could hardly
control the fingers that touched his magnificent face
wonderingly. Why was it that everything in the world
melted in this fire? It was wrong, yet it was so right, so
wonderful. He wouldn't let her go, holding her close as
though he couldn't get enough of her. Her nakedness felt
so vulnerable against the cotton and silk of his clothes.

'Daniel . . .' she pleaded. 'What's happened to us?'

'What we both have wanted since the minute we laid
eyes on one another.' This time his kiss was
intoxicatingly gentle, his lips teasing and caressing as
softly as the touch of a moth's wing. The savage
masculinity had become a tenderness that melted her

bones inside her, that dissolved her resistance. Her whole being was concentrated on the warm, moist mouth against her own, the tongue that traced her lips, probing her inner sweetness, tasting her as though she'd been some exquisite flower.

His shirt had pulled open. He was tanned and lean and strong beneath it, the dark hair matting his broad chest, emphasising the muscular contours of his belly. An athlete's body, every muscle defined and iron-hard with exercise under her shaky caresses. He drew the swimsuit slowly over the curve of her hips, over her loins, her thighs, pulling the flimsy garment down until she was utterly naked against him.

She shuddered with answering need as his arms embraced her, his face pressing hungrily into the silky plane of her belly, a pagan worshipping the statue of his goddess. Yet she was no statue, but a living woman, a woman whose response was instinctive and primal. His hair was thick and crisp under her fingers, every nerve in her body stretched tight with an expectation that was almost fear.

'Lili,' he murmured, his mouth roaming over her skin, touching the curve of her hip-bones, her thighs, her loins, adoring her silk-smooth skin. 'My beautiful, adorable Lili.'

Her mind wasn't functioning. Could it really be true? *Was* this what she'd desired, from the start? Or was she being bulldozed into something that was terribly wrong by a man whose motives she knew so little about?

She'd never felt anything like this hunger before, this need to possess and be possessed. Her head arched back as he kissed her erect nipples, his teeth and tongue teasing the aching peaks until she could bear it no longer. It was as though her veins were filled with liquid gold, as though she were melting inside, the perfection of her woman's body ready for love. Love with this man, this dark, potent stranger who was tearing her life apart as though he had the best right in the world . . .

'Tell me you want me.' His breath was ragged in his chest, his eyes smoky slits of desire. *'Tell me.'*

'It's wrong!' It was barely a whisper. 'You know how wrong this is!' Yet she couldn't stop her body arching to him as his hands roamed hungrily over her breasts, her flanks, the taut lines of her thighs.

'Then I'll say it,' he said fiercely. 'I need you, Lili. I'm getting so I can't live without you——' She gasped as his terrifyingly strong arms crushed her to him, her hands claiming the muscular curve of his back, the breadth of his shoulders.

With a desperate surge of energy, she pulled out of his arms and rose to her legs shakily. 'No,' she said in a barely-controlled voice. 'We can't do this, Daniel. I'm not that sort of woman, and I didn't think you were that kind of man.'

He stared at her naked body with hungry grey eyes, his broad chest rising and falling with the rough breath of passion. 'You know what kind of man I am,' he said fiercely. 'Are you prating of morality to me?'

'Yes!' She covered her breasts with trembling arms. 'I thought you were the most moral man I'd ever met! And I thought you were Martin's friend!'

She pulled her towelling robe clumsily around her slim, naked body, her eyes brimming with tears. The light fabric felt harsh against her ultra-sensitive skin. Desire was like a madness slipping away from her, leaving an ache that spread inside like a punishment. Mechanically, she picked up the nylon brush, and raked at her hair, oblivious of the golden tangles that caught.

'I never meant to hurt you.' He took her in his arms, holding her tightly as though to try and ease the pain he knew she must be feeling, caressing her cool cheek. 'Oh, Lili.' He kissed her bruised mouth tenderly. His eyes still held that stormy intensity. 'You can't deny the truth for ever, my love. One day, soon, you *will* be mine.'

It was as though her body were reluctant to obey her

commands. Where she had been so fluid moments ago, she was now stiff and clumsy. 'What have you done to me?' she whispered, her throat dry and ragged. It was incomprehensible that he should have such power over her feelings. She'd been caught up in a kind of madness back there. A madness she knew would return to haunt her, again and again.

Daniel buttoned his shirt, his black clothes now sombre in this white setting.

'So this is where you are.' They both turned sharply as Martin wandered into the pool-room, a towel slung over his shoulder. His hair was tumbled and untidy. He was wearing only a pair of Bermuda shorts. 'I couldn't sleep,' he yawned laconically. 'Too tense, I guess. Your apples all right?'

'They'll be ready for harvesting soon,' Daniel answered in a dry voice.

Martin nodded indifferently, then plunged into the pool, and started paddling towards the other side, spouting water.

Lili's eyes met Daniel's hotly. If Martin had come in a few moments earlier, he would have seen them. And that, she had no illusions, would have spelled the end of her relationship with Martin Petrov.

She stooped to snatch up her wet costume, then turned to him with brimming eyes. 'You won't be happy till you've broken us up, will you?' she demanded in a fierce whisper, and ran from the room to the only refuge she had.

She didn't go with them to the track on Friday morning.

She was simply too wound up to trust herself. Between her anxieties about both of them, and the potent way Daniel was now affecting her, she knew that an explosion of tension lay just beneath the surface. The incessant noise of racing-engines, the pressure of public scrutiny, would all be burdens she could do without.

On top of it all, the weather had become grey and drizzly overnight, which boded ill for the race. In the wet, the fast, twisting track would be all the more lethal.

Martin and Daniel were home just before lunch, bringing Derek and six or seven of the administrative staff for a final conference. The grid positions were now established, and inspired driving had given the Maison Rouge car a position at the very front of the pack. Yet Martin seemed more depressed than ever.

Alone with him in the study while the others talked in the dining-room, she laid a gentle hand on his arm.

'My ring is so beautiful, Martin. I've never even had a chance to thank you properly for it . . .'

'Oh, that.' He glanced at it. 'Yeah. It's nice.'

'You shouldn't have spent all your money, my love. It was an unbelievably generous thing to do.'

'As a matter of fact, that was for Daniel's benefit. To tell the truth, I got it on tick, the way Daphne Lawrence suggested.'

'But I thought Daniel wouldn't let you get into any debt?'

'He doesn't own me,' Martin said sharply. 'There are ways and means.'

'So all that romantic stuff about the old jeweller——' she began, half-amused, half-shocked.

'For public consumption.' Moodily, he turned to the window, and stared out at the fine drizzle that was clouding the beautiful gardens of L'Hermitage. He was wearing riding-boots and jodhpurs, and a chunky sweater that she'd bought him in Florence. 'As if I haven't got enough troubles, it has to rain.'

'What do you mean, "as if you haven't got enough troubles"?' she asked.

He hunched his shoulders. 'I've been struggling with the car. They've increased the power for Le Mans. Some new fuel injection system. No one bothered to consult *me* about the change.'

'You'll only need practice,' she tried to comfort him. For the first time in over a month, it was raining. Martin had been tense and depressed over the past weeks, but at least he'd turned to her now, as though needing her companionship at last. She thought of that afternoon at the pool. It would have destroyed him if he'd come in too soon. 'Promise me you'll take it easy, Martin.'

'I don't have much choice,' he said tersely.

'What do you mean?'

He studied her soft pink mouth and wide eyes briefly, then shrugged. 'I spun the car yesterday.'

'Oh, no!' She faced him unhappily. 'You didn't tell me! Were you hurt?'

'Only my pride,' he admitted with a sour smile. 'I went past Pollentier—the Belgian who crashed that Renault on the S-bend. Saw the smoke and the ambulances. Just lost my nerve, I guess. The tail simply broke away on the bend, and the next thing I knew I was on a very fast merry-go-round. Thank God I didn't hit anything, and I just reversed back on to the track and drove on. But it was nasty.'

'Oh, Martin!' And she'd been sitting with Daniel at *Les Hunaudières*, Martin the last thing on her mind. 'You might have injured yourself badly!'

'I almost wish I had,' he said with reckless depression. 'Now they won't let me take it faster than a crawl.'

Lili's green eyes clouded. 'Is Derek worried about you?'

'Daniel's probably been talking to him.' Martin's expression was savage. 'He wants to give me even less of a crack at the race. They're talking about giving me three hours out of the twenty-four. *Three hours*. I don't even know if I'll bother to pitch up!'

'I've never known you like this,' she said in concern. 'Come and talk to me properly.' She pulled him over to the leather chesterfield, and curled up beside him, tucking her slender, grey-stockinged legs beneath her. The fire crackling in the grate bore testimony to the coldness of the day.

'Everything's going wrong.' He leaned his elbows on his spread knees, gazing gloomily into the fire. Sometimes his profile had a hint of Daniel's about it, a touch of the same brooding elegance. 'I can't handle the Porsche, I've lost my touch. The whole team thinks I'm some kind of irresponsible kid.' He shook his tousled head. 'On top of it all, Daniel's stepping up the pressure on me to quit racing. After Le Mans.'

'You mean he's given you some kind of ultimatum?'

'He says he doesn't trust me after that spin. "Have your last fling at Le Mans. Then settle down. Or else."' It was a fair imitation of Daniel's deep, accented voice. 'He says he's let me go so far, but after Le Mans it has to stop.'

He picked up a copy of a racing magazine that was lying on the coffee-table, and rolled it into a truncheon. 'I feel like I'm at bay the whole time, Lili,' he said, his voice almost tearful. 'I'm just about ready to pack the whole game in, the way Big Brother wants me to.'

'Oh, Martin.' She didn't know how to comfort him. He seemed to lack some kind of inner strength, some independence of spirit. 'You once said you'd never let him bully you into submission.'

'He's too strong.' Abruptly, he flung the magazine into the fire. The red racing-car on the cover curled blackly in the hungry flames. 'And I'm frightened.'

'What of?'

'Of the car.' He seemed to have to drag the words out of himself. 'Of myself.'

She hugged him tightly, her cheek against his temple. 'Did the spin upset you?' she asked gently.

'It wasn't exactly pleasant,' he retorted sourly. 'I've never felt out of my depth before, but on Friday . . .' He twisted his hands together. 'I thought I'd finally found something I could do, something that didn't need him to show me the way. But I wonder whether I haven't been fooling myself again.' The curl of his mouth was self-pitying, unhappy. 'Maybe Derek just gave me that job to keep me under Daniel's wing.' He rubbed his eyes with his palms, sighing. 'Maybe the whole thing's been a sham from the start.'

'How can it have been?' She hated to see his self-confidence ebbing away like this, she had to do something. 'What about Silverstone? No one in their right mind would have put you in a racing-car if you didn't have enough skill to drive one!'

'It isn't just my skill.' He had the same sombre expression in his eyes that Daniel had worn after he'd asked her not to wear Martin's ring. 'Daniel suspects my commitment. That's even more important than skill. Anyone can drive a car, Lili, even a Porsche 962.' He looked at her with miserable blue eyes. 'It's having the dedication, the courage, to drive it to the limit, all the way. I mean, look at Bruno and Christian. They just don't seem to feel fear. I do! Why?'

'I have to live with it, too.' He snorted disbelievingly, but she grasped his wrists, forcing him to listen. 'Every time you're out on the track, I'm terrified you won't come back. And if you do become a professional racing-driver, I'll have to live with that fear.' Her face was serious, her eyes glinting emerald intensity. 'It's not exactly my choice of a pleasant married life. If driving's your career, what you really need to do in life, then I'll stick it out, for your sake. But if you don't feel safe any more, then maybe you *should* give it up. Swallow your pride. Join the company——'

'Be a good little boy,' he cut in acidly. 'Get a proper job, jump to Big Brother's orders. Yeah, yeah, I've heard it all before, baby. I don't need you to take his side against me again.'

'I'm not taking his side!' To her dismay, she was losing him again.

'Then why aren't you on my side?' He stood up

restlessly, and pulled on the silver anorak that was lying on the floor. 'I'll decide after Le Mans. I'll know then, one way or the other. But it'll be *my* decision. Not something you, or your good friend Daniel, have forced on me!' The sound of the zip was like a full-stop to their moment of intimacy. 'I'm going up to Ambrières. The local polo club are playing at two, and I've been invited to join in.'

'I wondered why you were all togged up in riding boots,' she smiled. 'What about the conference they're having in the dining-room?'

'It's just a load of guff about team-spirit,' he said scornfully. 'Honestly, Derek's like something out of the ark. All that team-spirit stuff went out twenty years ago. There *are* no teams any more. It's all just big money chasing advertising revenue. Out on that track, it's each driver for himself. Derek gets on my nerves sometimes!'

'Well,' Lili said gently, 'I suppose the fresh air will do you good.' She started getting up. 'I'll come with you.'

'No.' He shook his head. 'Look at the weather—it'll be all mud and sweaty ponies. And I'd probably fall off if I knew you were on the sidelines. Anyway, you'd be bored.'

'I won't be!'

'Well, I don't want you there,' he said flatly. He blew her a casual kiss. *'Ciao.'*

He walked out. Lili lay back against the leather, staring up at the beamed ceiling. Why did he have to be so callous with her?

Her fiancé, the man she'd once thought her perfect mate, was like a stranger to her these days. When she investigated her feelings for him, the strongest of them all was pity. What Daniel had told her about his mother and father had given her an insight into Martin that nothing else could have done. In a way, he'd always had a cloud over him. But unlike Daniel, he'd never struggled against that defect of birth. And of the two,

there was now no doubt in her mind which was the
better man.

Would Martin really leave racing? Her feelings were
ambiguous about that. Undeniably, it would be a relief
not to have to go through this constant tension. Yet it
would also be another capitulation, another thing he'd
tried and abandoned. How had Daniel put it? *Fallen in
and out of love*.

And if he did leave racing, she wondered where he
would go. To Maison Rouge maybe, but she doubted
that. Daniel was right—Martin didn't have any
vocation, any qualifications for life.

Would he expect her to live on his allowance from
Daniel? Or would he put their weddding-date back
again, and again after that, and again . . .?

She was linked to a drifting man. The thought
arrived with a wave of melancholy. When she'd
dreamed of her perfect man, he'd always been a rock, a
man whose stability she could cling to. Someone like
Daniel.

She pushed the useless thought away. Daniel could
never be hers while she was engaged to Martin.

She couldn't remember ever having felt this confused,
this torn. Was she really ready to give the rest of her life
to Martin Petrov? The way he reacted to pressure was
disconcertingly childish, the way he behaved sometimes
cut her to the quick. Yet she'd once loved him, or so
she'd thought.

If only he had some of Daniel's maturity. Daniel was
adult, male, in a way that Martin would never be. She
knew that by now.

Yet it would be cruelly disloyal to complain to Daniel
about Martin, go to him for advice.

Daniel . . . always her thoughts turned back to him.
She'd lived in his château, had eaten at his table, had let
him kiss the secret, silky skin of her body—and there
was always something between them. Something she
couldn't define, some potent quality that made him

mysterious to her, mysterious, and so devastatingly attractive.

'The carnival is over.' Derek Brundle was racked with tension as he stared through the plate-glass window of the hospitality lounge. 'Two minutes to three.'

The cars, massed on the grid, were a chequerboard of colours. Daniel was in the front rank, the sun dazzling on the scarlet and gold Porsche.

It all reminded Lili of some heraldic display, some convocation of mediaeval knights before a monstrous joust in the afternoon.

She'd been sitting silently with Martin and Christian Seberg, watching the circus which preceded the start. A parade of veteran cars, a group of parachutists making a drop on to the track, to be greeted by the bosomy welcome of bikini-clad glamour girls.

And the crowds! Sabrina Hobbs reported that almost three hundred thousand people were cramming the circuit, a mass of people like nothing Lili had seen before, some of them climbing to the dangerous heights of flagpoles to get a better view.

The roar of the engines was swelling to a deafening pitch, even through the concrete and insulated glass of the packed Maison Rouge lounge. Lili could make out Daniel's helmet through the windshield. She watched the hand of the big square clock tick inexorably towards three o'clock, and tried to form the words of a prayer for his safety.

The lights on the track flashed from red to amber, than a second later to green. Naked aggression erupted like a volcano as the cars surged forward. Unleashed, the pack leaped towards the first bend, a torrent of highly-tuned engineering bent on only one thing— winning at all costs.

For a few seconds the stream of cars raced by them. Then the canyon between the grandstands was empty.

'Now,' Derek Brundle said, releasing a pent-up breath, 'it's a question of waiting.'

She'd never anticipated how afraid for Daniel she was going to be. She couldn't relax for a moment of the next three hours, watching the track with haunted eyes as the cars surged past. She felt some relief when the crowded pack slowly spread out as the faster cars forged ahead, giving more room. But the two real dangers of Le Mans—the hours of darkness, and the widely differing speeds of the cars, were still to come.

Martin was keyed up as he waited for Daniel to come in, late in the afternoon. Lili could see his hands shaking as he pulled on his gauntlets. 'Will I get another drive after this?' he asked Derek intently.

'That depends on several things,' Derek said quietly. 'We'll see how this spell goes. Okay, Daniel's built up a slight lead, but that means nothing at this stage. Remember what we decided in practice—don't push it too hard, understood?'

'Yeah,' Martin nodded. He barely seemed to notice Lili as she kissed him. 'I'll be fine,' he nodded impatiently in answer to her anxious question. 'Just fine.' He pulled his helmet on. She'd already realised that she had to keep outwardly calm, knowing her fear would only be an added burden.

She stood holding his gauntleted hand tightly until the red and gold Porsche pulled off the straight and into the pit-lane, where the refuelling crew were waiting to perform their well-rehearsed task.

Daniel's black-clad figure emerged from the narrow doorway, and Martin was climbing behind the wheel. Lili watched, heart in mouth, while Daniel shouted advice to Martin over the noise of the engines, one gloved hand on Martin's shoulder.

Then Martin was driving the Porsche out into the track again. She felt like a traitress at that moment, torn between her fear for Martin and her piercing relief that Daniel was back safely, if only for the time being.

Daniel stood watching the car out of sight, then unfastened his helmet and pulled it off. The concentration was almost frightening on his dark, harshly chiselled face. He stood for a minute with Derek Brundle, intently discussing the car's performance. Then he was walking over to her.

Nothing on earth could have stopped her from throwing her arms around him and holding him tight.

'*Chérie,*' he said softly, caressing her hair with rough tenderness, 'take it easy!'

'I don't think I could bear many more of these,' she said tautly. He smelled wonderful, of man's hair and man's skin, underlying the harsh reek of oil.

'Come and make me a cup of coffee,' he commanded huskily.

His arm tight around her waist, he walked with her to the luxurious trailer behind the grandstand that served as a rest-area. She didn't care if Derek and the crew *were* watching them; if she needed an excuse, then the danger facing Daniel was as good as any.

She knew in her heart that he was going to kiss her again as the door closed behind them. This time she was reaching to slide her arms round his neck, her mouth opening of its own accord under that sweet onslaught. She was hungry for his kiss, aching for him, like she'd been for days, weeks. It had been torment to have to sit and wait and do nothing, and now that he was here, nothing mattered any more, not even the fact that Martin was out there...

His hands slid down her back as their kiss deepened, pulling her close until her breasts were crushed against his chest. It was so good to admit her need for him at last, simply to drink in the passion he was offering her without question, to let the desire run like wildfire in her blood.

Daniel pulled her down on to the couch, his mouth still locked to hers. His hands were hungry as they traced the slender contours of her body. 'You're in my blood,' he said roughly. 'I think I could kill to have you, Lili.'

'You don't have to,' she promised him, all her restraint seeming meaningless now.

'I'll hold you to that,' he promised in a deep growl.

A knock at the door heralded Christian Seberg, bringing Daniel a beaker of bright red fluid.

'Glucose,' he smiled, 'courtesy of our manager. You're driving like an ace, Daniel. Keep it up.' If he was surprised to find Lili here with Daniel, he gave no sign apart from a brief smile before he left again.

'I'm going to change my suit,' Daniel told her, draining half the glassful in one swallow. 'Pass me another from the locker, *chérie*.'

She got the black, asbestos-fibre suit out, and unfolded it, then turned on the electric percolator for his coffee. When she turned, he had stripped almost naked, only slim briefs containing his manhood, and her heart jolted at the smooth, tanned wonder of his skin. So strong, so taut with potent male power! The hair across his chest and flat belly was black, black as sin, crisp under her fingers as he came to her again, drawn by the look in her eyes.

'*Lili* . . .' She could feel the tension in him, as though he were struggling with some overwhelming force inside him, having to restrain himself from simply taking her, here and now. The thought made her weak, frightened and yet thrilled beyond belief.

He unfastened her blouse, his eyes almost fierce as the silk rustled aside, revealing the hardening peaks of her upward-tilting breasts. 'God,' he whispered, 'you're so beautiful, Lili. The most beautiful woman I've ever seen . . .'

She moaned, helpless, as he kissed the smooth skin, tasting her, teasing the tight buds of her nipples into an ache of excitement. She ran her fingers through his thick, dark hair. Hair that smelled so good, demanding her fingers to pull—his mouth became almost cruel with desire, making her gasp. Did he have any idea what he was doing to her? It had never been like this with

Martin, not *remotely* like this maelstrom! Yet not even
guilt over Martin could dull this moment for her.

The rumble of the percolator brought her shakily
back to reality. She pulled away from him, and poured
him a mugful, the way he liked it, hot, strong and
sweet.

'Lili, are you all right?' His thumb brushed wetness
off her cheek, and she realised that she was crying, her
eyes blinded with tears.

'I—I'm fine,' she said unsteadily. The woman in her
was reeling, the rules she'd been trying to live by all
these weeks in ruins around her. She clung to him as he
comforted her with astonishing gentleness.

'It's all right,' he said quietly, running his hands
through her silky hair with infinite tenderness.
'Everything's all right, my love.'

She looked at him with eyes that were soft as
mountain mist, and touched his cheek, her slim fingers
gold against the rugged bronze of his skin.

'I'm so afraid for you,' she confessed. 'It's hard to
bear. Be careful out there!'

'This is my last Le Mans, Lili.' She saw by his eyes it
was the truth. 'My last race.'

'You'd be bored stiff without this,' she laughed
unevenly. 'What will you have to provide excitement?'

'You,' he said softly, holding her eyes with his.
'You'll never stop exciting me, Lili.'

There was another knock at the door, and he pulled
away, smiling at her tenderly. 'This isn't the time or
place for love, is it?' He turned to the door, dressing.
'What is it?'

'NBC television,' came Sabrina Hobbs's voice. 'Can
they have an interview, Daniel?'

He grimaced at Lili. 'See what I mean? You'd better
get some coffee down as well, *chérie*. It's going to be a
long night.'

Confusion, noise, lights searing the darkness. Lili

reached for Iko's arm as they fought their way through the press of people, not wanting to be separated from her. Over the noise of the crowd, the incessant howl of the cars, seven hours into the race, was like a pagan litany.

Iko had found Lili sitting tensely alone in the crowded lounge. Daniel was driving again, Martin and Christian Seberg asleep in the trailer. 'Come out of your privileged little enclave,' she'd invited, 'and see the *real* Le Mans.' Glad of any distraction, Lili had come.

Crossing the bridge was difficult, there was such a crowd of people. On the other side of the track, the neon-lit ferris-wheel towered over the funfair. It was almost a vision of Hell, Lili thought, listening to the screams of people on the rides and watching the glittering blades wheeling through the night.

The air was pungent with the smells of roasting meat and petrol, the acrid smoke of Gauloises, hot dust, the scent of pine-needles. The smells of Le Mans.

As they reached the S-bends, a group of three cars came snarling over the brow of the hill, their powerful twin headlights carving the darkness like knives. Lili flinched as they exploded past her and Iko, blue and yellow tongues of flame fluttering at each set of exhaust-pipes, making the night hideous for a few seconds before they were gone.

'What on earth makes them flame like that?' Lili asked in awe.

'Something to do with the turbochargers,' Iko said.

Two more cars hurtled past them, the din of their engines hurting Lili's ears. It was impossible to make out the numbers, so any one of these monsters could contain Daniel.

Iko crouched as the next group of cars blared past them, swinging her lens to track after them.

The sheer scale and complexity of Le Mans was bewildering. So many cars, so many teams and drivers, such a long race—it was an event composed of a thousand different stories, each with its own drama and humour.

'Maison Rouge are still in the lead,' Iko called over the bawling PA system, 'but the Rothmans Porsches are creeping up. How's Martin?'

'Sleeping—but very tense,' Lili said.

'I can imagine.' Iko smiled briefly. 'Drivers get unbelievably tense during a race as long as this. I've seen tough men burst into tears like children.' She fiddled with her camera. 'Think he'll cope?'

'I hope so,' she nodded.

'I couldn't help noticing the way Daniel looks at you,' Iko said. Lili said nothing, feeling a prickle down her spine. Iko swivelled to track after two Lancias, their Martini stripes lurid in the fierce glare of the headlamps. 'Watches your body. Watches your face.'

'There's nothing in that,' Lili said, keeping her voice light. 'Men are always looking at women, it doesn't matter who or how old.'

'I work for Daniel,' Iko said simply. 'I've never seen him look at any other woman like that.'

'I want a cup of coffee,' Lili said, changing the subject bluntly. The grateful darkness hid the fact that her face was hot with embarrassment. 'I'm going back to the grandstand to get one.'

'Hold on,' Iko pleaded, grabbing her gear as Lili stalked off. 'I'm coming. Listen, I should have kept my big mouth shut. I'm sorry. But if ever you want to talk about him—or about Martin—I hear all the company gossip. Okay?'

'Okay,' Lili said briefly, not quite sure how to take that. 'Come on!'

CHAPTER NINE

LILI must have fallen into an uneasy sleep some time in the early hours of the morning. She was curled in an armchair in the hospitality suite, her cotton anorak wrapped around her shoulders, when Derek Brundle shook her out of confused dreams.

'Lili! Wake up!'

'What—what is it?' She sat up, mind still muzzy, and pushed the golden hair out of her eyes. Through the windows, the sky beyond the deserted grandstands was steel-blue, pre-dawn.

'There's been a crash. A bad one.'

She was fully awake now, her heart pounding like a hammer in her chest. She'd dreaded this, known it would happen. 'Martin.'

'No.' Derek shook his head, looking drawn and old. 'Martin wasn't in the car, Lili. It's Daniel.'

'Daniel!' Cold fear clutched at her, crushing the words in her throat. 'Is he—alive?'

Derek shook his head helplessly. 'Don't know yet. It's out on the Mulsanne.'

Lili was on her feet, praying it was a nightmare she'd soon awaken from. *The Mulsanne*. A crash on the Mulsanne straight was what the drivers dreaded; the terrible speeds loaded the odds against survival.

It was cold out in the pit-lane. The mechanics were huddled in a silent group around their equipment, listening to the commentary blaring over the public address. A glance at the track was enough to tell that something was horribly wrong. Yellow flags were up all the way along the barriers. The cars were moving at half-speed in the dim light, following obediently behind the big Mercedes-Benz pace-car, the flashing amber

155

lights on its roof forbidding any overtaking until the
danger was past. Like a funeral procession.

Christian Seberg was sitting on a pile of tyres, his
head brooding on his folded arms, his face expressionless.

'Lili!' Martin, his Nomex suit greasy and sweat-
stained, had arrived from the trailer where he'd been
sleeping. His face was grey, his hair tousled and dirty.
'Daniel's crashed the car.'

She nodded, speechless. He looked like a dazed child
now, his world shattered. Painfully, she was reminded
of her own feelings when Joan Lucas had died, her own
desolation and grief.

No! She mustn't think like that. He was alive. He *had*
to be.

'The car's wrecked,' Martin said numbly. 'The
announcer said so, I can't believe it. It could have been
me out there!'

'Is that all you can think about?' Derek snapped at
him, but Martin seemed not to hear.

'Can we get out to him?' Lili asked, her voice quiet
and controlled.

'It must have happened somewhere in the woods past
Les Hunaudières,' Derek said tersely. 'If so, we can get
there.'

'There's nothing we can do——' Martin began.

'For God's sake, let's go,' Lili cut through his
sentence, already running to Derek's car.

The area round *Les Hunaudières* was chaotic.

Beyond the police cordon, the very trees were on fire,
smouldering debris lodged high in their branches.
Marshals were struggling to drag the wheel-less wreck
of a blue and yellow Lancia off the track.

There were two more cars sprawled in the woods,
beyond the buckled barrier. Lili had to press her
knuckles to her mouth to bite back the scream.
Crushed, flattened, gutted, they bore no resemblance to

the brilliant machines that had started the race half a day earlier.

There were medics and police crowded round the Maison Rouge car, recognisable only by the tatters of red and gold glass-fibre bodywork still intact. It was far more badly damaged than the other car.

White with shock, she pushed past the men round the wreck, desperate to see into the cockpit.

Daniel was pinned in the crushed cabin, one arm outflung. She couldn't see his face through the crazed visor of his helmet, but a nurse was checking an intravenous drip in his right arm.

'Is he alive?' she implored the bearded paramedic next to her.

'Yes, *mam'selle*,' he nodded grimly. 'He is conscious. But he is trapped in the car, and we have no way to get him out until the special equipment arrives to release him.'

'Can you get his helmet off?' Derek Brundle was at her side, pale as a ghost.

'It is safer to keep it on until he is free,' the medic advised.

'He wants it off,' Lili said urgently, seeing Daniel tugging weakly at the chin-strap. Willing hands reached in to ease the helmet off.

Beneath the tan, Daniel's face was drained of colour. His eyes were dark as they met hers, and tried to smile.

'Hello, *chérie*. I'm sorry about this . . .'

'You're going to be all right,' she promised him unsteadily. 'How—how badly are you hurt?'

'Numb,' he said, closing his eyes briefly. 'Very cold. I feel frozen . . .'

She turned imploringly to the medic as Daniel's eyes closed again. 'What's the matter with him?'

The medic lowered his voice. 'His blood-pressure is very low. We think he is bleeding internally. One of the internal organs——' He obviously couldn't find the English word. *'La rate.'*

'The spleen,' Lili whispered.

'*Exactement.*' He tapped his own body. 'Here. We are giving him plasma,' he said, indicating the clear bag of fluid being held aloft by one of the other ambulancemen. He turned to the officer beside him with a crackle of French.

'What's he saying?' Martin asked Derek, looking white and desperately nauseous.

'They think his spleen is ruptured,' Derek said tightly. 'They think he's lost up to two litres of blood already, and they don't know when the special equipment will get here.' He hesitated, the blue flashing light of the ambulance flicking monotonously across his face. 'They think he's dying.'

'No!' Lili's voice cracked. This was how her mother and father had died, for want of blood on a stretch of tarmac. 'He mustn't die!'

'I can't stand much more of this,' Martin said, his voice gagging. 'I can't bear it.' He took her awkwardly by the arm. 'Let's get out of their way and wait.'

'Don't you *care* about him?' Eyes blazing, she shook off his hand and swung round to the medics. 'Can't you stop the bleeding?'

'He needs a surgeon,' he said quietly. 'We do not carry blood, only plasma. Blood must come from the *centre de transfusion sanguine* in the village.' He pointed to the names painted on the buckled door. Next to Daniel's name were the letters *AB Rh neg*. 'When they have lost as much as two litres——' He shrugged. 'Plasma is not enough to maintain the vital organs.'

'I'm group O negative,' Derek said urgently. 'Universal donor. Can't you take a transfusion from me, here, and give it to him?'

'We are thinking of doing this now,' he nodded, pointing at a young *gendarme* who was standing by the car. 'This policeman has volunteered to give blood—he is also group O negative.'

Light exploded in Lili's memory. '*My* group's AB

Rhesus negative! I'm sure of it, *monsieur*—it's very rare, and I regularly give blood in England!'

He stared doubtfully from Derek to her. 'You want to donate your blood?'

'*Yes!*'

'The correct blood would be best. But the chances are very slim. It is like trying to fill a bucket with a hole in it, you understand?'

'Try it,' Derek said imperatively, 'for God's sake!'

'Okay.' Unceremoniously, the bearded medic started rolling up her left sleeve. 'We prepare.'

With unhurried efficiency, the team was suddenly in motion.

'You don't know what you're doing!' Martin stammered beside her, looking sick.

'I know exactly what I'm doing.'

'You don't know how much he needs.' His face was working, and he was obviously close to hysteria. 'By the sound of it, it's pouring out inside him——'

She barely felt the needle slide into her vein, the medic strapping it surely to her elbow.

'*Bien.* We take your blood into this bag first, *entendu*?'

Lili nodded. Someone brought a camp-stool for her, and she sank down as they began. The plastic tube seemed so terribly thin, a crimson thread leading from her arm to the little plastic bottle. And from there it would go into Daniel's arm. From her heart to his.

Time passed. As her blood began to slide into his veins, she saw Daniel's head stir, a faint flicker of his eyelids. Her arm was starting to ache, the thick needle buried deep in her tanned skin. She stared down at Daniel's face. How many emotions you've made me feel, she thought numbly, and I've only known you a few weeks.

'What will they be able to do at the hospital?' she asked, her voice dry and uneven.

'Take out the spleen immediately. For a fit young

man like this, no more serious than having his appendix
out. They can clamp the vessels and stop the blood
loss.'

Derek Brundle brought her a mug of sweet coffee
from somewhere, then squatted down next to her,
sliding an arm around her. 'I'll not forget this, Lili,' he
said quietly. There were tears in his eyes. 'Whether he
lives or dies, I'll not forget this.'

'He's going to live.' She tried to smile at him. 'I
promise you he will.'

Orange flashing lights were approaching now, as half
a dozen emergency vehicles arrived through the trees.

'Bloody marvellous.' Derek stood up, looking more
cheerful. 'They've brought the machine. We've got a
chance now.'

Arc-lights were being set up round the wrecked car,
turning night into noonday as a team pushed the jaws
of a powerful machine into the crushed doorway. With
a whine of electric power, the jaws dilated, bending the
tubular steel chassis open with deceptive ease. Medics
moved forward to ease Daniel past the splintering
fibreglass.

Then he was free, and being lifted carefully on to a
stretcher. The bearded medic had Lili's free arm in his
hand. 'Into the back of the ambulance,' he commanded.
'Prenez garde, mam'selle.'

'I'll see you at the hospital,' Derek called to her. 'I'll
bring Martin in the car.' She nodded without looking
back; whether in reaction to the shock, or due to the
blood she was losing, her legs were as wobbly as a
child's.

Rushing through the night, with the siren screaming
overhead, she watched while the bearded medic
examined Daniel.

'Will he live?' she asked tearfully.

'Je crois,' he nodded. 'Your blood is keeping him
going.'

'Here. *Mam'selle.'* Gently, another medic was wiping

the tears off her cheeks. 'Try and relax,' he ordered her compassionately. 'In a little while, it will be all right.'

Dawn was glowing brightly through the curtains of the waiting-room when the surgeon came in to find Lili. 'The operation has been a success. If you wish to speak to Monsieur Valais, he is conscious now.'

'You go,' Derek said to Lili gently. 'I'll wait here with Martin.'

The surgeon led Lili through the green double doors to the private surgical ward. 'I'm afraid you will only have a few moments,' he warned, and left her at the bedside.

Daniel's eyes were closed, and although the pallor was gone from his skin now, various drips testified to the seriousness of the accident. Hardly daring to breathe, Lilli took his hand, and leaned over to touch his forehead with her lips.

His fingers curled around hers possessively, smoky grey eyes opening to look up at her hazily.

'They tell me I have your blood in my veins now,' he said with the ghost of a smile.

'It's just a load of chemicals,' she smiled tenderly. 'I hope it does you some good.'

'It's not just a load of chemicals.' His fingers tightened around hers. 'It's alive. It's you. You've given yourself to me, my little one.'

'More Magyar mysticism,' she whispered, kissing his dry lips. 'All nonsense. Are you in pain, my love?'

'They'll give me something after you've left. I just wanted to see you first. And thank you.'

The look in his eyes made her heart flip over. 'How did the accident happen?' she asked, changing the subject. 'Can you remember?'

His lids dropped closed again. 'The car ahead lost a wheel. Just past *Las Hunaudières*. He couldn't control it. The Jaguar beside me hit him first, then we all went into the barrier . . .

'At two hundred and thirty miles an hour.' She had a vision of the scene. The blurring road ahead, brilliant in the headlights. A sudden swerve ahead, another car in the way. A desperate, split-second battle to keep the Porsche on the road. Then the terrible somersault over the barrier, the shattering impact——

'Do you know—how the other drivers are?' he asked, speaking with difficulty now.

'They're fine,' she told him, knowing she must go, no matter how much of a wrench it would be to leave him in this state. 'A broken arm, shock, nothing worse.' He nodded, and she bent to kiss him again. 'You must rest now. I'll see you tomorrow.'

'Lili——'

'What is it?' she murmured.

'Nous nous appartenons, mon amour.' His lips responded to her kiss. *'Je t'aime, Lili . . .'*

The doctor was at her side again, touching her arm. 'I think he should rest now, *mam'selle*.'

She nodded, not trusting herself to speak, and walked out into the corridor. 'We belong to each other.' That's what he'd said to her. 'I love you . . .'

Derek Brundle and Martin were waiting for her.

'He's going to be fine,' she told them, her green-gold eyes wet. 'I managed to have—have a few words with him. He looks well.'

'Thank God.' Derek kissed her cheek, giving her a quick, hard hug. 'You've saved a very special man's life this night. You're going to achieve many things, Lili. But whatever else they remember you for, a lot of people will always remember you for what you did at Le Mans. Listen, they want you to spend the night here, just to keep an eye on you. They've got a bed for you in a quiet private ward on the fourth floor. Okay?'

'Okay,' she nodded.

'Good. I'll wait for you downstairs, Martin. Don't be long.' He pushed through the door. For the first time,

Lili noticed that Martin was sitting with his head in his hands. She touched his shoulder softly.

'Martin? Are you all right?'

'It's gone,' he was mumbling, his voice muffled by his fingers. 'I know it, Lili. It's gone.'

'What?' She sat down beside him, trying to smile. 'What's gone?'

'My nerve. It's gone for good. I couldn't even drive to the hospital. Derek had to take me.' He held out his hands, showing her how they shook. 'It could have been me last night, Lili.'

'You're all right,' she said tiredly, pulling her tumbled hair away from her face. 'It was Daniel in the crash, not you.'

'That's immaterial!' She had never seen Martin so upset. 'I was driving last night, too. It could just as easily have been me!'

'Yes, I suppose it could,' she nodded, letting her mind go blank. She was too exhausted to try and work out his complex feelings at this stage. Like everyone else, he was strained this morning, tired and emotional. 'But it wasn't.'

He got out of the chair restlessly, and pulled the curtain open. The daylight stabbed into her eyes painfully. 'I'm packing it in, Lili.'

The jerky words registered dully. 'You mean you're leaving racing?' she asked.

'It's not for me, babe.' He opened his mouth to speak, then fell silent as a tall, blonde nurse came through the door.

'Mam'selle Bergman? Please follow me.'

'We'll talk about it tomorrow, Martin,' she said wearily, getting up to go. 'The main thing is that Daniel's going to be all right.'

'Yeah,' Martin said heavily. 'I guess that's the main thing.'

She was dreaming of Daniel, of swimming beside his

bronzed body in a deep blue pool, when the blonde nurse came in with breakfast.

'Ah,' she smiled, 'you look much better now. More like the Lili Bergman I have seen in the magazines.' She took Lili's pulse briskly, measuring it against the watch pinned to her starched breast, then nodded. '*Bien*. The doctor is doing his rounds, *mam'selle*. He will see you in a little while.'

'How is Daniel?' Lili asked, sipping the coffee gratefully.

'Monsieur Valais is much the same. He is a very strong man,' she said reassuringly, 'he will have no problems, I think—thanks to you.'

'Can I see him?' Lili asked pleadingly.

'As soon as the doctor has checked you over,' the nurse promised, 'but he will not be able to speak to you until he regains consciousness.'

'I just want to see him,' Lili smiled.

'I will arrange it.' She hesitated. 'Do you feel strong enough to have a visitor?'

'I'd like to wash my face and brush my hair first,' Lili said with a slight smile. 'Who is it?'

'A man from the police, mam'selle.' She passed Lili a small card. 'His name is Inspecteur Le Gros.'

'Is it about the accident last night?' Lili asked, studying the card in surprise.

The nurse shrugged. '*Je ne sais pas, Mam'selle Bergman*. Most likely.'

'If you'll give me a minute to tidy up, I'll see him,' Lili nodded. 'It's time I got up, anyway—there's no reason for me to stay in bed all morning.'

'Best wait until the doctor sees you,' the nurse advised. 'Stay in bed. I will send the *Inspecteur* up in five minutes.'

The French policeman was tall, bony, and red-haired, in his mid-forties. He sat down beside her bed, looking amicable but also serious.

'Thank you for agreeing to see me at such a difficult

time,' he said in flawless English. 'May I congratulate you on your gallant action last night?'

'You're very kind,' Lili said with an uncomfortable smile, 'but it was nothing, really.'

'I think you will find otherwise when you see this morning's newspapers.'

'Well.' She was feeling ten times better now that she brushed her hair and touched a little lipstick to her mouth. 'Did you want to speak to me about what happened last night?'

'No, *mam'selle*.' His eyes were light brown, intelligent. 'I wanted to ask you a few questions about your fiancé.'

'About Martin?' She shook her head in puzzlement. 'What about him?'

He cleared his throat. 'I understand that Monsieur Petrov recently gave you a diamond ring, of antique design.'

'Yes,' she nodded, green eyes darkening.

'May I see it?'

'Of course.' She held out her left hand, palm down. 'That's the ring.'

He stared at it for a moment, then passed her a Polaroid photograph. 'Would you say that was a similar ring?'

'It's exactly the same!' She recognised the unique setting of the stone at once. A heaviness had settled around her heart now. 'Where did this picture come from!'

'The ring in the photograph was stolen from a house in Tours a few weeks ago, together with several other valuable pieces of jewellery.'

'Oh, no!' She touched her cold lips with her knuckles. Her first instinctive thought was that Martin had lost his money. 'Then the man Martin went to must be a crook!'

'That is a possibility,' the policeman nodded. 'Did your fiancé tell you where he acquired that ring?'

'He said he'd bought it in an antique jeweller's, in *le vieux Mans*.'

Le Gros's eyes had the observant, clever look of a chimpanzee's. 'Did he tell you the name of the dealer?'

'No, he didn't.' Something in the tone of his voice had sent alarm-bells shrilling through Lili's mind. 'You don't think Martin *knew* it was stolen?' she gasped.

'No doubt there is a perfectly simple explanation. Have you any idea where we might find Monsieur Petrov?'

'He was here last night,' she said unhappily. 'I don't know where he went.'

'I'm afraid,' he said gently, 'that we will need the ring for our investigation.'

'Here.' She twisted the ring off her finger, and gave it to him. She hated the thought that it had belonged to someone else, had been stolen from another woman's home. 'Take it now.'

'I'd rather you delivered it to the *commisariat* yourself.'

'I don't want to keep it a second longer,' she said, her voice rising sharply.

'Very well. I'll arrange for the hospital authorities to keep it in their safe until the formalities have been arranged.' He took the ring, eyes softening as they examined her miserable, pale face. 'I want you to understand, *mam'selle*, that no shadow of suspicion or doubt rests on you. You do understand that?'

'Yes,' she nodded. As if that mattered to her.

'May I ask when you're planning to leave the hospital?'

'As soon as the doctor has seen me.'

'Where will you go then?'

'Back to L'Hermitage. I've been staying there. Then on Wednesday night, I'm flying back to London.'

He rose. 'Thank you for giving me your time. And I am sorry.'

Oh, Martin, she thought tiredly as the policeman left to arrange safe-keeping of the ring, *what have you done?*

She lay back on the pillows, remembering that Martin had already told one set of lies about the ring—

inventing a soft-hearted jeweller. If he *had* deliberately bought a stolen ring, she'd never forgive him. What if the police arrested him, though? It didn't bear thinking of. Martin might be a fool, but she couldn't believe he was dishonest, no matter how he'd betrayed her by his irresponsibility.

After a thorough check half an hour later, the French doctor pronounced her fit enough to leave as soon as she wanted. First, though, there was another visitor waiting to see Lili, a strikingly handsome middle-aged woman, dressed in a severe grey suit.

'My name is Bernardine Thévenet, Miss Bergman. I am Daniel Valais' personal secretary.' She sat down beside Lili, taking her hand with a motherly air and a waft of *Je Reviens* by Worth. 'You performed an act of great bravery last night, and many, many people are very grateful to you. I know that Daniel would want you to have access to all the help Maison Rouge can give you.'

'It's very kind of you,' Lili nodded, 'but I really think I ought to discharge myself this morning. The doctor tells me I'm fit to leave immediately.'

'Then I will settle the bill at once,' the secretary said decisively, 'and arrange for the helicopter to take you back to L'Hermitage.'

'There is something I would like you to do quite urgently,' Lili said, struck by a sudden thought. 'Do you think you could locate Martin Petrov, *madame*?'

'*Certainement.* Do you want to see him?'

'I want you to give him an important message.' There was no way of making it sound discreet. 'Tell him that the police want to question him about the ring.'

'The police?' An instant frown creased the handsome features. 'Have the police been here to see you?'

'They took my engagement ring away,' Lilli said tiredly. 'Martin bought it for me a few days ago, and there's some suspicion about it. They want to interview him.'

'Ah, *quel dommage.*' Regret made Bernardine Thévenet look suddenly older. 'The ring is stolen?'

'They think so,' Lili said. 'Apparently——' Before she could continue, the door opened, and Iko Shikura arrived, looking summery in powder-blue.

'How's our heroine this morning?' she said brightly. She had an armful of newspapers. 'Read all about yourself! *Bonjour*, Bernardine.'

'*Vous avez vu Martin Petrov?*' the secretary asked.

'Not since the early hours of this morning,' Iko said. Her face grew serious as she noted the expressions on Lili and Bernardine Thévenet's faces. 'What's the matter, Lili?'

'Oh, Iko.' She'd wanted to keep it to herself, but it was such a relief to talk to a friend that the whole story spilled out of her. Iko listened with intent eyes, then sat down tiredly on Lili's bed beside the secretary.

'That's a pity,' she said quietly. 'But it was inevitable. He always did sail too close to the wind.' She met Lili's dark, cloudy eyes. 'You might be getting some insight now into why they call him *Martin le Malencontreux*. He does tend to have this unhappy knack.'

'You mean this has happened before?' she asked in disbelief. Bernardine Thévenet merely tightened her full lips, but Iko nodded.

'Once or twice. Bernardine probably knows a lot more about it than I do. There was a fuss some months ago about a car, and before that, some other piece of jewellery. Martin can't resist a bargain.'

'Iko, I'm engaged to be married to him.' Helplessly, Lili looked from one to the other. 'You don't think he knew that ring was stolen?' she asked, echoing her question to Le Gros of an hour ago.

'He does know the sort of people who have access to stolen goods,' Iko said unemotionally.

'What are you saying?' Lili demanded unhappily. 'How do you know that?'

'I went out with Martin once or twice, long before

you met him. You can ask Bernardine.' The secretary
nodded silently. 'There's always a criminal fringe that
likes to hang around rich young men like Martin Petrov
and his circle.'

'I don't know what to say,' Lili said, her voice
catching.

Iko looked at Bernardine Thévenet as though she
were bracing herself for something. 'Lili, I still don't
think you know everything about Martin.'

'Like what?' Lili demanded in dread.

'Bernardine,' Iko said, her eyes pleading with the
older woman, 'no one has told her yet. Don't you think
she has a right to know?'

'To know what?' Lili asked urgently, feeling like
someone standing before a locked door.

Bernardine Thévenet sighed. 'Martin Petrov had a
relationship some time ago, Miss Bergman. A young
Belgian woman he met while he was at the Sorbonne.
From this relationship——' she hesitated '—a child was
born.'

'*What?*' Lili felt as though she'd just been kicked in
the stomach. 'You can't possibly mean——Martin? A
child?'

'A little girl,' Iko said, her golden face calm and
unsmiling. 'He was engaged to marry the woman when
she became pregnant. He changed his mind about the
marriage, dropped out of university, and left her flat.
She didn't have any family, so she had to go back to
Antwerp and apply for welfare there.'

'I can't believe it! He would have told me,' she said,
almost pleadingly.

'It's meant to be a big secret,' Iko said. 'He even
imagines Daniel doesn't know about it.'

'And does he?' Lili asked, trying dazedly to take it in.

'Daniel has been supporting them for the past three
years.' Bernardine smiled gently. 'Martin Petrov has
never sent them a single franc, and the woman is
apparently too proud, or too shy, or perhaps even too

fond of him, to try and get maintenance through the French courts.'

'Daniel has been giving the mother a generous monthly allowance,' Iko put in. 'That's how Bernardine learned about it—Daniel told her some of the story.' She sorted absently through the newspapers she'd brought, looking down. 'I found out separately. The woman's sister happens to be working in Paris. She's friendly with someone who knows a friend of mine.' She shrugged. 'I couldn't go out with him after I knew. I once told you I hear all the gossip, Lili. But this story happens to be true.'

Lili sat in stunned silence. Her mind still hadn't been able to take it in. It was like an ugly fantasy, a story about someone else. Was Martin really capable of that kind of behaviour? In her heart, beneath the initial shock, she knew he was. Why hadn't he told her? Why hadn't he said *something*?

'I knew he hadn't told you,' Iko said, touching Lili's hand, 'when you made that remark, about neither of you being interested in children, at the race-track. I wanted to tell you about it a couple of times since then, because you were my friend, and because I thought you had a right to know. But I also wondered whether he would tell you himself.'

'I thought he might have changed,' Bernardine said unhappily. 'This business shows he has not.'

'Yes,' Lili said tightly. 'Yes, I suppose it does.' Anger was balling inside her at the way she'd been lied to. And not only by Martin.

Daniel had known all about Martin. Daniel had known about the child, had known exactly what sort of person Martin Petrov really was—and he'd concealed it from her.

'I've been fooled,' she said in a low bitter voice. 'Fooled by both of them. I can understand Martin concealing this,' she went on grimly. 'I suppose I've known for a long time what he's really like. You can make excuses for his weakness. But Daniel—I thought he had some respect for me!'

'I think he feels more than respect,' Iko said, sending Bernadine a quick glance.

'Even if he didn't, I thought at least he was a truthful, honest man. How could he hide something like this from me?'

'Martin Petrov is Daniel's only true blood-relative,' Bernadine Thévenet reminded her quietly. 'It may have been hard for him to tell you——'

'To tell me the truth,' Lili supplied as Bernadine ground to a halt. Bitterness washed over her. For all his disapproval, for all his anger over Martin's irresponsibility, Daniel had been more loyal to his cousin than to her when it came to the push. 'I can't believe that I've been so deceived about Martin.'

Iko nodded, her mouth turning down sadly at the corners, giving her the look of a tragic Kabuki mask for a moment. 'I didn't want you to know about the child out of spite, Lili. I wanted you to know just how capricious and unpredictable Martin really is. I know it's heart-breaking to say these things, but I think that marrying him would be the most terrible mistake you could ever make.'

'Marry him?' Lili echoed dully. 'I don't think he ever intended to marry me. I think he just wanted a love-affair. And when he couldn't have that, he wanted me around to give him a bit of moral support against Daniel.'

'He's used more than one woman in that way, Lili, including me,' Iko said. 'But I would give him the benefit of the doubt and say that he probably cares for you as well.'

'He doesn't love me,' Lili said flatly. 'He doesn't love anybody.' The decision had crystallised in her mind. 'I'm going back to London tonight, Madame Thévenet. Will you help me to get ready?'

The secretary's eyes widened. 'If you wish it, of

course. But the doctors say that Monsieur Valais will probably regain consciousness by this afternoon. If you would just wait, speak to him before you go——'

'No, I don't want to speak to him. Nor to Martin,' she added sharply as Bernardine's mouth opened to argue further. 'If you see him before the police do,' she said with a touch of acid, 'you might warn him that they're looking for him.'

'Mam'selle Bergman,' the secretary said, looking alarmed now that she saw how serious Lili was, 'I would strongly advise you to remain in Le Mans for at least another twenty-four hours!'

'If you don't want to help me,' Lili said, with a calmness born out of anger, 'I can easily manage on my own.'

'She means what she says, Bernardine,' Iko told her quietly.

'Very well,' the secretary capitulated reluctantly. 'Would you like me to book you on a flight to Heathrow this evening?'

'Yes, please,' Lili nodded. The only emotion she felt now was relief at the thought of leaving France and getting back to London. Lili met the other woman's eyes. 'I'm grateful for your help, *madame*. And I appreciate your concern, but I simply want to get home as soon as possible.'

'As you wish.' Bernardine Thévenet rose, looking as if she rather dreaded what Daniel would say to her when he'd recovered. 'I shall leave you to dress, Mam'selle Bergman.'

'What about Martin?' Iko asked, when the Frenchwoman had left.

'What about him?' Lili replied shortly, starting to pull on the clothes she'd taken off last night. Her shower could wait.

'Well, all you know is what Bernadine and I have been able to tell you. You should ask him to tell you his side of the story.'

'He should have told me his side of the story when he asked me to marry him,' Lili pointed out. 'But if he does have anything to say to me, he knows where I live in England. And right now, I just want to get back there.'

'And your engagement?' Iko asked, helping Lili get the anorak over her painful left arm.

'Don't be silly,' Lili said tiredly. 'It never was an engagement. Martin had no more intention of marrying me than of flying to the moon. I was just his latest hobby, and I'm only sorry it's taken me a month to find that out.'

'Lili,' Iko said, stopping her with a gentle hand, 'I don't know what's between you and Daniel. I can only guess. I know it's a complex situation, and I shouldn't intrude, but I have this intuition that you and he care a great deal about each other.'

Lili shook her head. The depth of her own feeling for Daniel made his betrayal all the more hurtful. 'If you'll forgive me, I don't really want to talk about either of them any more.'

'Then let me do the talking,' Iko pleaded. 'As I saw it, your engagement to Martin was the only thing that was stopping you and Daniel from getting together. I could see that at Le Mans. I wanted to talk to you then, but we hadn't seen each other for a year, and—well, I didn't. But now there's nothing to keep you and Daniel apart.'

'Is it really that simple?' Lili asked ironically.

'It could be! If you'd only speak to him.'

'No,' she said decisively, brushing her white-gold hair in the mirror. Her face was pale, determined. She felt she could never forgive Daniel for the way he'd hidden the truth about Martin from her. He'd had so many opportunities to tell her, and had never done so. It was *that* which hurt, not Martin.

Ironic, Lili thought painfully. She'd been trying to hide her growing feelings for Daniel so long; and now that she was able to admit to her passion at last, it had been obliterated by an act of betrayal. 'I don't want to see him, not ever again.'

'But maybe you owe it to him.'

'Owe it to him?' Lili snapped, turning to Iko with a passionately curling mouth. She'd been made a complete fool of for a month now, and it hurt like hell. 'I've given him my blood, for God's sake, both physically and emotionally. I don't owe him *anything*!' She was close to tears, and she didn't want to cry now, or she knew she'd never get to London.

'You're making the biggest mistake of your life.'

'Look, if Daniel wants me, he can come and get me! Now *please*,' she said, drawing a shaky breath, 'will you either help me, or go away!'

Iko scurried to help her pack.

CHAPTER TEN

'LEFT shoulder up please, Lili. Mouth relaxed. That's beautiful.' The shutter whirred smoothly as Jerry took the shots. 'Chin up a little, please. So, how was Barbados?'

'Hot,' Lili said, knowing a monosyllable was all that was expected of her. It seemed impossible that only three or four weeks had slipped past since she'd come back from France that blustery Sunday night, leaving Daniel, the ruins of her engagement to Martin Petrov, and a painful clutter of emotional debris behind her.

Since then, she'd been all the way to Paradise Beach, Barbados, and back.

'Okay, that'll do. Can we have the next necklace, please?'

The deputy manager of Van Impe's came forward, reverently unfolding the black velvet parcel. 'This is the "Mary Rose",' he told them plummily. 'Forty-two carats, and quite, quite flawless.'

Lili couldn't see Jerry's face past the spotlights, but she knew he'd be wearing an ironic smile. Still, the commission couldn't be more prestigious. Van Impe's specialised in rare and priceless jewels, and they'd insisted on Lili Bergman to model some of their finest gems for *Vogue*.

'It's one of my personal favourites,' the diamond-merchant said, looping it around her neck. A pink teardrop the size of a thrush's egg on a string of rose-cut blue-whites. Against her tanned skin, the jewellery looked gorgeously opulent. She was sitting in a high-backed chair, with a mock eighteenth-century military dress-coat draped around her shoulders, all gold-braided epaulettes and embroidered facings. Apart from jeans, which wouldn't show in the shots, she was naked underneath it.

'What's that worth?' Jerry asked from the darkness while Susie Knight, his assistant, adjusted the diamond against Lili's naked throat. 'Half a million?'

'Something in excess of that,' the jeweller said smugly. Lili tried not to let her calm expression drop. No wonder there were two armed security guards posted outside the studio door. The deputy manager of Van Impe's himself had arrived in the back of a Securicor van with the gems.

'Well,' Jerry directed drily, 'try and look as though you've just been given it for Christmas. Slight smile, Lili. Calm, aristocratic. That's good. Look straight into the lens, please.'

Lili focused her gaze on the clear glass of the lens, the muted light caressing her skin. Damn Daniel! She hadn't been able to get him out of her mind for a single day of the past month. As her mind had cleared, a part of her had been waiting for a word from him, some apology, some message——   •

'Three-quarters profile, please. Chin up again.'

But there had been no word from Daniel. Nor, for that matter, from Martin.

Her own emotions had made Barbados an ordeal. Chiefly her swelling hurt and anger that Daniel hadn't bothered to make contact with her, not even to give her some thanks for helping to save his life.

She'd even had to phone Mandy Collins from Bridgetown to get the news that Daniel had left hospital, and was making a good recovery. He might at least have told her *that*. She'd been sick with worry and guilt those first few days.

Yes, her abrupt flight from France had been a foolish gesture, but if he had cared a damn for her, he could easily have understood that. Sent her a message. It would have been a simple matter to trace her to the hotel in Bridgetown where she and the GKZ crew had been staying.

That silence had been one of the cruellest things ever done to her.

The fact that she hadn't heard a word from Martin, either, was unimportant. Looking back, it was easy to see how they'd both been caught up in a spiral of excitement and glamour. They'd been like two children, chattering of marriage and a life together; she hadn't been ready, and she doubted whether Martin Petrov would ever be ready. He was little more than a naughty, irresponsible boy. He had probably felt the same relief at the break-up of their engagement as she had.

Jerry studied her face through the lens, then shook his head. 'I think we're going to have to change your make-up for this one, Lili. At least the lipstick, anyway. Something pink, Susie, to match the stone.'

Lili sat passively while Susie Knight completed the make-up. Her outward poise concealed the desert of loneliness she'd been living in these past few weeks. She'd never believed she could have missed anyone as much as she missed Daniel. Missed his voice, the smell of his hair, the way he smiled.

Missed the way they'd desired one another with that urgent, flooding passion. There were nights, even now, when her need for him was like a drug in her veins. It intoxicated her, filled her dreams with a passion that awoke her, her body quivering like a violin under the vibration of the bow.

The man from Van Impe's was murmuring something to Jerry, who called to her from the darkness beyond the spotlights.

'Lili, you've rather too much breast showing. Pull the lapel over please, Susie. Right. Can you lean back, love, let the stone rest against your throat.'

The vision of Daniel had made her ache now, that old, sweet ache that nothing could soothe except the touch of his lean, muscular body. She closed her eyes, tilting her head back so that her hair cascaded in gold down her back, her lips parting moistly.

'That's it,' the jeweller said excitedly. 'Exactly what I had in mind!'

She barely heard. It was strange how modelling liberated her mind, bringing the memories up, sharp and clear as reality. She would never forget how beautiful he'd been, seeing him in her mind's eye in a hundred different settings, a hundred different memories.

There, on the marble by the great glass-vaulted pool, lying in the great splash of sunlight, that had been almost the most perfect moment of all. Brief, agonisingly brief moments of love snatched through the hot, silent afternoon. How overwhelmingly sweet it had been!

Memories. The texture of his skin, so fine, so bronzed against her own. His body, demanding, intoxicatingly potent, thrilling her so sweetly . . .

'You're working beautifully,' Jerry said in the pause as they moved on to the next stone. 'Was it hard to adjust to movie work?'

'Not really.' It was an effort to bring herself back to the present. 'No, not really. Everyone was very helpful.'

'I was talking to Nick the other day, and he dropped some hints that he wants you for another television feature later on in the year.'

'I know,' she nodded. Jerry didn't make any more conversation. He knew her well enough to know she wasn't in the mood. She hadn't told him what had happened to her in France, but most of the modelling world had an inkling of some kind. Ironically, most imagined she'd been jilted by Martin, and was pining for him.

'This is our *pièce de résistance*,' the diamond-merchant said smoothly, unfolding yet another square of black velvet. 'It's simply called the Biarritz stone.' The diamond blazed under the lights, an exceptionally deep, heart-shaped stone hanging from a thin ribbon of pearls like a drop of the sun itself. 'Just over sixty carats, and flawless.'

'Wow.' Even Jerry was impressed this time. 'That is beautiful. How much is it worth?'

'Well,' the man from Van Impe's smiled, looping it around Lili's slender neck, 'we're talking oil-money.' He tilted his head, studying the diamond against Lili's skin. 'Very beautiful indeed. It's on sale for one million two.'

'I'm afraid it isn't.'

The deep voice floated on the darkness, husky and unmistakable. Lili's heart had leaped into her throat, but disbelief paralysed her. She'd subconsciously heard the studio door open and close, but it hadn't registered until now. The man from Van Impe's squinted against the bright lights.

'I beg your pardon? Who said that?'

'I did.'

Lili felt a wave of faintness cross her heart. It *had* to be, no one else in the world had a voice like that.

'And if you'll excuse me,' Jerry said in puzzlement, 'who the hell are you?'

'I'm the man who has just bought the Biarritz stone.' Daniel strolled out of the shadows into the pool of light. Lili could only stare up at him, knowing she would never see a more beautiful man as long as she lived. He was wearing the charcoal grey suit he'd worn that first day at L'Hermitage, a red rose at his lapel. And those smoky, utterly male eyes were smiling down at her, making her heart spin dizzily. 'It looks rather well on her, don't you think? It's my wedding-present to Lili.'

'Everybody hold on!' Jerry pushed his glasses up into his curly hair. 'Who is Lili going to marry?'

'She's going to marry me.'

'This is some kind of joke,' the man from Van Impe's said uncertainly. 'It must be.'

Lili clung to Daniel as he smiled gently at the astonished faces in the studio. 'I'm very sorry,' he said softly, 'but Lili Bergman has another engagement right now.'

'I haven't finished my shots!' Jerry exclaimed as Daniel held out his hand to Lili. 'You can't just take her away!'

'But I can,' Daniel growled. 'And I am. And unless I am very much mistaken, this is the last commission Lili will ever undertake.' He stared into her eyes with an intensity that shook her to her core. 'From now on,' he said in a gravelly voice that was meant for her ears alone, 'the only diamonds you will wear will be your own. And the only man you will wear them for will be me.'

'On one condition,' she said in a shaky voice.

He drew back his hand, and rested it on his hip. One dark brow arched as if in amusement at her temerity. 'And what's that?'

'That you never get into another racing-car, as long as you live. I'm never going through all this again for the sake of arrogant male ego!'

'I thought I'd told you at Le Mans,' he said gently. The others were sitting riveted by this extraordinary exchange, but neither she nor Daniel cared. 'That was my last race. Ever. And that's a solemn promise, *chérie*. I only enjoyed racing when there was no love in my life. Now——' He smiled into her eyes. 'Now there's you.'

'Daniel,' she whispered, 'what took you so long? I've nearly died without you!'

Strong arms reached for her as she rose giddily; and then she was in his arms, her mouth surrendering to his in thoughtless, fierce bliss.

'We can discuss that somewhere else,' he said, crushing her against him hungrily. 'But right now the Ferrari is double-parked outside this studio and having spent one million two hundred thousand pounds on your wedding-present, I have no wish to add a parking fine. Come, *chérie*.'

'You're not leaving!' The man from Van Impe's flung himself at the door. 'Guards! Help!' He recoiled as a white-haired man pushed past him. 'Oh—I'm terribly sorry, Mr Van Impe——'

'You're so clumsy, Fothergill,' the white-haired man snapped, then beamed at Daniel, holding out a thick white envelope. 'Monsieur Valais—the authentication and export papers for the Biarritz stone.'

'Thank you.' Daniel pocketed the envelope, then turned to take her arm again. 'Shall we go?'

'That jacket isn't mine!' Jerry protested weakly. Susie Knight was staring at Daniel with shining eyes and open mouth. She was obviously going to dine out on this story for years. 'I had to hire it in especially!'

'Send the bill to Maison Rouge,' Daniel said calmly.

'At least let me take a photograph.'

Lili was so shaky she had to lean against him as they walked through the arched doorway.

'Daniel,' she said faintly, 'I'm not exactly dressed to appear in public!'

'You should have thought of that earlier.' In the corridor outside, he turned on her with eyes that glittered like sabres. 'If you ever show your breasts to another man again,' he growled fiercely, 'I'll lock you in your bedroom for a month!'

'It was only in the line of work,' she laughed weakly, adoring him. 'And I wasn't showing them, only hinting.'

'Confine your hinting to me from now on.' His arms crushed her to him in a long embrace that went some way to soothing the ache of desire for him inside her. Then they were walking out into the busy street, a man in an exquisite charcoal grey suit, a woman in jeans, a military coat from a bygone age, and a million-pound diamond.

'You haven't really bought this stone?' she demanded dizzily as she curled up against his side in the Ferrari.

'Did you think I was joking?' he asked, arching one dark eyebrow.

'But it's impossible!' She lifted the heavy stone in numb fingers. 'A million pounds? I'm not even worth a fraction of that, my love!'

'You're worth a million times that,' he said huskily, sliding an arm round her waist to pull her closer. 'Call it a little thank-you for what you did for me at Le Mans.'

'Oh, that.' She closed her eyes in bliss, snuggling up against him as he drove. 'A simple matter of saving your life. You still haven't explained what *kept* you for three and a half weeks! I spent every night in Barbados dreaming of you, and every morning I'd run down to reception to see if there was a letter from you. I thought I'd lost you—how could you do that to me?'

'There was a minor matter of recovering from my operation,' he smiled.

'You were back home and walking after three days,' she accused. 'I called the hospital.'

'Also, you needed a little time to cool off,' he added. 'According to Bernardine Thévenet, you were in a white-hot rage when you left Le Mans. I didn't want to spoil everything by coming for you too soon.'

'And Martin?' She sat up, looking at him. 'What has happened to him?'

'He's gone to the United States for a rather long holiday.' Daniel showed no regret. 'A holiday designed to avoid the keen interest of the French police, that is. The young fool bought you that ring from a well-known receiver of stolen goods in Tours. One of his more disreputable acquaintances. If I hadn't given him the money for the air-fare, he'd probably be in jail right now.'

'At least he's not in the Bastille,' Lili sighed. 'He has a great gift for landing on his feet.'

'Or someone else's.'

'What on earth possessed him to do such a crazy thing in the first place?'

'He can't resist a bargain,' Daniel smiled.

'Yes, but he didn't have to buy me a ring!'

'To be frank,' Daniel said, 'I think he wanted to get out of the relationship by then. He'd realised he was out of his depth with you, that you weren't just another good-time girl out for a little fun with no strings attached. You'd taken his offer of marriage seriously, and that had begun to frighten him. Martin intends having a lot more fun out of his life yet.'

'So?'

'So the ring was something in the nature of a buying-off present. Something to soften the blow when he announced he was leaving.'

'The cheek of it!' Lili exclaimed. 'And *I* was thinking about leaving *him*!'

'Anyway, the last time I saw him he was very subdued. He asked me to convey his apologies for any trouble caused.' He shot her an ironic gleam. 'Et cetera, et cetera.'

'Oh, I find it hard to stay cross with him. What will he do?'

'He plans to stay in New York until the fuss dies down. The racing idea is over, too. He's managed to get a job with some kind of pop-recording studio, and is apparently eyeing out the local talent. No doubt he'll be "engaged" again before long.' Daniel sighed. 'Maybe he'll have grown up a little by the time he gets back to France. But that won't be for a long time, yet.'

'And the team? Is it all finished?'

'Don't be silly,' he smiled. 'Crashes are part of the scene in motor-racing. Derek's already got two new cars. He's got high hopes of winning the Spa 2000 in a week's time—though I doubt we'll be there to watch.' He glanced at her wickedly. 'We'll be far too busy.'

'By the way, where are we going?' Lili asked, waking up to some sort of reality and looking out of the window.

'To your flat, in Tunbridge Wells,' he informed her calmly. 'We're spending the night there, then in the morning we're going back to L'Hermitage to start planning our wedding.'

Lili couldn't hold back the gasp as she walked through

the door of her flat, later in the afternoon. She'd never seen so many red roses in her life.

There were mountains of them, their velvety crimson blooms glowing from every table, every available bit of hall space, every ledge or sill. Their dark perfume was heady on the air, intoxicating as wine.

'Oh, my love,' she whispered. 'What have you done?'

'I had them empty every florist's from London to Brighton,' he smiled, slipping strong arms around her waist. 'I'm afraid I had to tell your caretaker I was going to marry you before he'd let me into the flat. You don't mind if he was the first to know?'

'Mr Norris? No, I don't mind,' she said weakly. 'It looks as though I was destined to be the last to know, whatever happened.'

There were more roses in the passageway. Her bedroom was filled with them, too—and her bed was a sea of rose-petals, scattered deep in fragrant abundance.

'I've always dreamed of making love to you in a bed of rose-petals,' he said gently. She seemed to have no bones as he laid her down on the bed, easing the lapels of her jacket aside to expose the perfect curves of her naked breasts. 'Unless,' he paused, 'you would rather wait until out wedding-night?'

'Considering that I've been waiting for you for twenty-three years, my love,' she smiled hazily, 'another few weeks doesn't seem very long.'

'Another few *weeks*?' he repeated in a tiger's growl. 'I thought you had red blood in your veins!'

'You ought to know,' she retorted. 'On the other hand,' she relented, twining her hands round the bronzed column of his neck, 'perhaps you could try and persuade me otherwise . . .?'

She knew that dark, compelling look of desire so well—and this time there was to be no resisting, no barrier to stop them. That thought sent a shudder through her, making his lips curve in a smile.

'What is it?'

'Just you. I don't know much about love, Daniel. You'll have to teach me.'

'I intend to teach you,' he assured her softly. 'Everything.'

'You make me giddy.' She touched the heart-shaped diamond that lay against her skin on its ribbon of pearls. 'It's magnificent,' she said with a shaky smile. 'Only you, my love, could give such a precious gift.'

'When I found out you were going to be modelling stones from Van Impe's today, I went to the shop in Knightsbridge and chose that diamond. What appealed to me was its purity, its flawlessness. Like yours, my love.' He brushed the soft skin of her breasts with hungry lips, making her moan softly, her fingers pressing into the broad, muscular back beneath the charcoal silk. '*À propos* of modelling—there's no question of your continuing to work once we're married,' he informed her with a flinty light in his grey eyes. 'It's not that I'm a selfish man, but I'm a very jealous one. I don't intend to share you with *anyone*. Is that very arrogant?'

'You're the only man I've ever met,' she whispered, 'who has all the right in the world to be arrogant. I love it.'

'Will you enjoy being mistress of L'Hermitage?'

'If it doesn't over-awe me,' she nodded with a smile. 'Oh, darling, I just pray that I'm going to be worthy of you!'

'I want you so badly, Lili. I've wanted you ever since the day Martin brought you to L'Hermitage. If I hadn't known in my heart he had no intention of marrying you, I think I'd have pushed him into the moat!'

'You wouldn't have!' She had to look deep into the dark, pagan depths of his eyes to see whether he was teasing or not—and even then, she wasn't quite sure! She pulled at his tie, unribboning the red silk. 'Why didn't you tell me about his having made that woman pregnant, and then abandoning her?' she asked.

'Well, if you remember, I did try and instil some doubts in your mind about Martin's ultimate lack of responsibility,' he reminded her.

'But if you'd told me the whole truth, you could have settled Martin as a rival any time you wanted!'

'Could I?' His quirked brow challenged her. 'I'm a great believer in giving a man enough rope.'

'What does that mean?'

'It means,' he grinned, pulling off his jacket and unfastening his shirt, 'that if I'd told you too soon, you might—in your blessed purity—have forgiven the young scamp. But the longer he tried to hide it from you, the more furious you'd be when you eventually found out—and the better my chances of snatching you away from him would be.'

'You Machiavellian *devil*,' she gasped. 'I've never known anyone as ruthless as you!'

'It took nerve,' he admitted. His body was just as she'd remembered it, potent and utterly male. The scar of his operation was still livid against the deeply bronzed skin. She touched it with compassionate, caressing fingers. 'There were times I thought I'd explode with frustration,' he went on. 'I was like a man holding an ace in the biggest poker-game of his life, and having to contain myself until the moment was ripe.' An ironic chuckle rumbled in his deep chest. 'And when the moment did come, I was unconscious in a hospital bed, with a tube going down my throat!'

'Do you remember what you said to me that night?' she whispered, as he kissed her arched throat, his tongue tasting her silky skin.

'Of course.' She could hear the smile in his voice.

'Say it again,' she pleaded, her fingers lost in his dark hair.

'*Nous nous appartenons, mon amour*. We belong to one another, Lili, for ever.'

'You've forgotten something,' she accused dizzily, her breath close against his commanding lips.

'I have not. *Je t'aime, Lili . . .*'

She closed her eyes, feeling her heart turn over inside her. 'Those words sound so sweet to me, my love,' she whispered. 'I'm almost afraid I've died and gone to Heaven.'

'That's nothing,' he promised huskily, 'to the way you're going to feel in a few heartbeats' time.'

'*Je t'aime aussi,*' she whispered against his descending mouth. '*À tout jamais.* Is my French right?'

He didn't answer. And as their bodies met, touched, kissed, it hardly seemed to matter. She had the rest of her life to get an answer.

ROMANCE

ROMANCE

Next month's romances from Mills & Boon

Each month, you can choose from a world of variety in romance with Mills & Boon. These are the new titles to look out for next month.

THE TULLAGINDI RODEO Kerry Allyne
WALK INTO TOMORROW Rosemary Carter
DANCING IN THE DARK Pippa Clarke
HIDDEN TREASURES Emma Goldrick
PLAIN JANE Rosemary Hammond
TRY TO REMEMBER Vanessa James
MAID TO MEASURE Roberta Leigh
PASSIONATE VENGEANCE Margaret Mayo
BACHELOR IN PARADISE Elizabeth Oldfield
BITTER LEGACY Sandra K. Rhoades
*THE GLASS MADONNA Liza Manning
*FANCY FREE Karen van der Zee

Buy them from your usual paperback stockist, or write to: Mills & Boon Reader Service, P.O. Box 236, Thornton Rd, Croydon, Surrey CR9 3RU, England. Readers in South Africa — write to: Independent Book Services Pty, Postbag X 3010, Randburg, 2125, S. Africa.

*These two titles are available *only* from Mills & Boon Reader Service.

Mills & Boon
the rose of romance

Take 4
Exciting Books
Absolutely
FREE

Love, romance, intrigue... all are captured for you by
Mills & Boon's top-selling authors. By becoming a
regular reader of Mills & Boon's Romances you can
enjoy 6 superb new titles every month plus a whole
range of special benefits: your very own personal
membership card, a free monthly newsletter packed
with recipes, competitions, exclusive book offers and
a monthly guide to the stars, plus extra bargain offers
and big cash savings.

AND an Introductory FREE GIFT for YOU.
Turn over the page for details.

**Fill in and send this coupon back today
and we'll send you
4 Introductory
Doctor Nurse Romances yours to keep
FREE**

At the same time we will reserve a
subscription to Mills & Boon
Doctor Nurse Romances for you. Every
two months you will receive the latest
6 new titles, delivered direct to your door.
You don't pay extra for delivery. Postage and
packing is always completely Free.
There is no obligation or commitment –
you receive books only for
as long as you want to.

It's easy! Fill in the coupon below and return it to
**MILLS & BOON READER SERVICE, FREEPOST, P.O. BOX 236,
CROYDON, SURREY CR9 9EL.**